Key Stage 2 Maths

WORKBOOK **2**

Numerical Reasoning Technique

Dr Stephen C Curran

with Katrina MacKay

Edited by Andrea Richardson

This book belongs to

Accelerated Education Publications Ltd

Contents

Chapter Two
ADDITION

1. Single-digit Addition

Addition is the process of counting two or more groups of things together to make a new total. This applies to any object, image or number.

This is often represented in a number sentence, such as:

$$\overset{\text{U}}{4} + \overset{\text{U}}{3} = \overset{\text{Units}}{7}$$

This calculation gives the same answer when written the other way round.

$$\overset{\text{U}}{3} + \overset{\text{U}}{4} = \overset{\text{Units}}{7}$$

Number sentences use mathematical symbols.

The symbol for 'add' is +.

The symbol for 'equals' or the outcome of the calculation is =.

a. Basic Addition up to 9

Example: Add the dots in the two squares and write the number sentence.

Count the dots in the first square: . There are **4**.

Count the dots in the second square: . There are **2**.

Altogether there are **6** dots.

The number sentence is: **4 + 2 = 6**

Answer: **4 + 2 = 6**

Exercise 2: 1 Add the items and write the number sentence:

1) <u>5</u> + <u>1</u> = ___

2) ___ + ___ = <u>2</u>

3) ___ + ___ = ___

4) ___ + ___ = ___

5) ___ + ___ = ___

6) ___ + ___ = ___

7) ___ + ___ + ___ = ___

8) ___ + ___ + ___ = ___

9) ___ + ___ + ___ = ___

10) ___ + ___ + ___ = ___

A number line is a useful tool for adding number sentences.

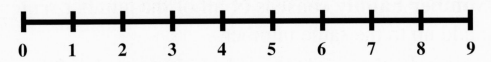

Example: Use the number line to calculate **4 + 3**.

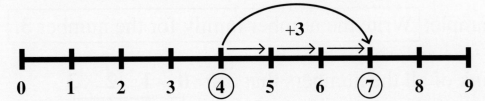

Start at **4** and count **3** places forwards along the number line to reach **7**.

The number sentence is: $4 + 3 = 7$

Answer: **7**

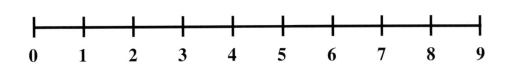

Exercise 2: 2   Use the number line above to answer the following:

1) $1 + 4 =$ ___

2) $3 + 2 =$ ___

3) $5 + 2 =$ ___

4) $2 + 7 =$ ___

5) $4 + 4 =$ ___

6) $6 + 1 =$ ___

7) $1 + 8 =$ ___

8) $7 + 1 =$ ___

9) $3 + 5 =$ ___

10) $2 + 7 =$ ___

Score

b. Number Families up to 9

A **Number Family** consists of all of the number sentences that add up to the same number.

For example, the number family for the number **2** is:

$$0 + 2 = 2 \qquad 1 + 1 = 2 \qquad 2 + 0 = 2$$

Example: | Write the number family for the number **3**.

Think of all the numbers that can be added together to make **3**.

Start with **0 + 3 = 3**, then work through the number combinations.

There are four number sentences.

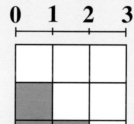

$$0 + 3 = 3$$
$$1 + 2 = 3$$
$$2 + 1 = 3$$
$$3 + 0 = 3$$

Score

Exercise 2: 3a

Complete the number sentences:

1) Write the five addition pairs for **4**.

Shade in half of the grid to help identify the number family of **4**.

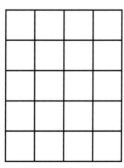

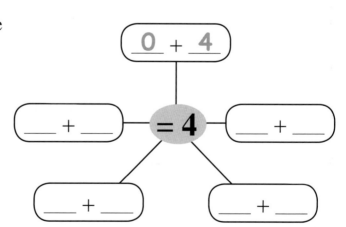

$$\underline{0} + \underline{4}$$

$$\underline{\quad} + \underline{\quad}$$ $= 4$ $\underline{\quad} + \underline{\quad}$

$$\underline{\quad} + \underline{\quad}$$ $\underline{\quad} + \underline{\quad}$

2) Write the six addition pairs for **5**.

Shade in half of the grid to help identify the number family of **5**.

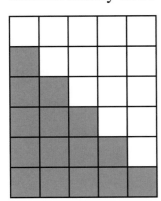

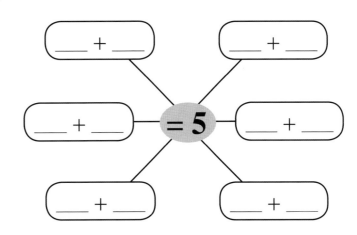

3) Write the seven addition pairs for **6**.

Shade in half of the grid to help identify the number family of **6**.

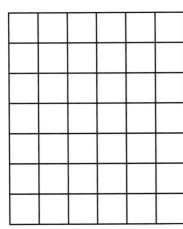

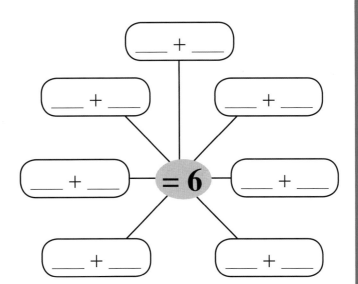

4) Write the eight addition pairs for **7**.

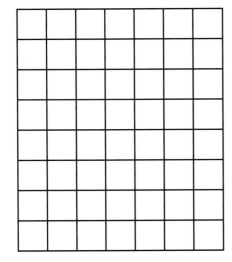

_____ + _____ = _____

_____ + _____ = _____

_____ + _____ = _____

_____ + _____ = _____

_____ + _____ = _____

_____ + _____ = _____

_____ + _____ = _____

_____ + _____ = _____

5) Write the nine addition pairs for **8**.

_____ + _____ = _____   _____ + _____ = _____

_____ + _____ = _____   _____ + _____ = _____

_____ + _____ = _____   _____ + _____ = _____

_____ + _____ = _____   _____ + _____ = _____

_____ + _____ = _____

6) Write the ten addition pairs for **9**.

_____ + _____ = _____   _____ + _____ = _____

_____ + _____ = _____   _____ + _____ = _____

_____ + _____ = _____   _____ + _____ = _____

_____ + _____ = _____   _____ + _____ = _____

_____ + _____ = _____   _____ + _____ = _____

Example: | Complete the number sentence: $2 + \underline{} = 5$.

This is one of the number sentences in the number family of **5**.

By looking at the number family, it can be seen that the missing number is **3**.

$$0 + 5 = 5$$
$$1 + 4 = 5$$
$$\boxed{2 + 3 = 5}$$
$$3 + 2 = 5$$
$$4 + 1 = 5$$
$$5 + 0 = 5$$

Answer: $2 + \underline{3} = 5$

Exercise 2: 3b   Complete the number sentence:

7) a) $4 + \underline{} = 6$ b) $\underline{} + 2 = 2$

   c) $7 + 2 = \underline{}$ d) $1 + \underline{} = 3$

8) a) $\underline{} + 0 = 1$ b) $4 + 1 = \underline{}$

   c) $3 + \underline{} = 8$ d) $\underline{} + 1 = 7$

Example: Link the two numbers that add up to **4**.

Using the **4** number family, look for the numbers within the circle that form a correct number sentence.

$$0 + 4 = 4 \quad 3 + 1 = 4$$
$$1 + 3 = 4 \quad 4 + 0 = 4$$
$$2 + 2 = 4$$

Answer: $3 + 1 = 4$

Exercise 2: 3c Link the two numbers that add up to:

9) a) **2.** 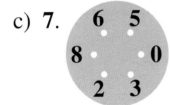 b) **6.** c) **7.** 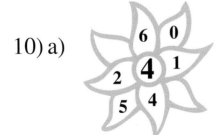 d) **3.**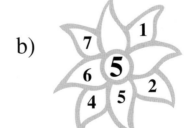

Shade in the two numbers that add up to the number in the centre of the flower:

10) a) b)

c)  d)

c. Addition in Words up to 9

There are many different terms for addition. Here is a list of the most commonly used terms:

- Add
- Plus
- Total
- Both

- Increase
- Enlarge
- Combine
- Altogether

- Find the total of
- Find the sum of
- More than
- In all

Example: | Find the total of **seven** and **two**.

Convert the words into a number sentence. 'Find the total' is the same thing as using the + sign between two numbers. The number sentence is $7 + 2 = 9$ or **seven** plus **two** equals **nine**.

Answer: **9**

Exercise 2: 4   Answer the following:

1) Increase **6** by **3**.   _____

2) Find the total of **4** and **4**.   _____

3) What is **one** and **two** altogether?   _____

4) What is **3** plus **4**?   _____

5) Combine **4** and **5**.   _____

6) What is **two** more than **four**?   _____

7) Find the sum of **3** and **5**.   _____

8) Add **2** and **3**.   _____

9) Increase **three** by **one**.   _____

10) Find the sum of **2** and **5**.   _____   **Score**

d. Single-column Addition up to 9

Addition can be shown as a number sentence, for example:

U   U Units
$$3 + 4 = 7$$

It can also be shown as standard column addition.

Units
$$\begin{array}{r} 4 \\ 3\ + \\ \hline 7 \\ \hline \end{array}$$

When doing column addition, place the largest number at the top and the other numbers in size order beneath.

Example: | Calculate 5 + 4. |

$$\begin{array}{r} 5 \\ 4\ + \\ \hline ? \\ \hline \end{array}$$

5 is the larger number, so it goes on top.

5 units add **4** units is **9** units.

Answer: **9**

U
$$\begin{array}{r} 5 \\ 4\ + \\ \hline 9 \\ \hline \end{array}$$

Exercise 2: 5   Calculate the following:

Score

1) $\begin{array}{r} 5 \\ 2\ + \\ \hline \\ \hline \end{array}$
   2) $\begin{array}{r} 3 \\ 1\ + \\ \hline \\ \hline \end{array}$
   3) $\begin{array}{r} 2 \\ 2\ + \\ \hline \\ \hline \end{array}$
   4) $\begin{array}{r} 6 \\ 3\ + \\ \hline \\ \hline \end{array}$
   5) $\begin{array}{r} 4 \\ 3\ + \\ \hline \\ \hline \end{array}$

6) $\begin{array}{r} 1 \\ 1\ + \\ \hline \\ \hline \end{array}$
   7) $\begin{array}{r} 4 \\ 2\ + \\ \hline \\ \hline \end{array}$
   8) $\begin{array}{r} 7 \\ 1 \\ 1\ + \\ \hline \\ \hline \end{array}$
   9) $\begin{array}{r} 4 \\ 2 \\ 2\ + \\ \hline \\ \hline \end{array}$
   10) $\begin{array}{r} 5 \\ 3 \\ 1\ + \\ \hline \\ \hline \end{array}$

e. Single-column Addition above 9

When an addition in the units column is greater than **9**, the tens are carried over to the tens column.

```
  T U
    8
    7 +
  ___
  1 5
  ___
  1
```

For example, **8 + 7 = 15** which is greater than **9**. **15** is **1** ten and **5** units, which means the **1** is carried into the tens column.

Example: | Calculate **9 + 5**. |

Step 1 - Add the units column.

        9 units plus **5** units is **14**.
        This is **1** ten and **4** units.

```
  T U
    9
    5 +
  ___
    4
  ___
  1
```

        Write a little **1** under the line.
        This is called **carrying**.

Step 2 - There are no tens to add, so the carried ten is moved into the tens column.

```
  T U
    9
    5 +
  ___
  1 4
  ___
```

        9 + 5 = 14

Answer: **14**

Exercise 2: 6 Calculate the following:

Score

1) **6**
    5 +
___

2) **9**
    4 +
___

3) **8**
    7 +
___

4) **7**
    5 +
___

5) **5**
    5 +
___

6) **7**
    6 +
___

7) **8**
    6 +
___

8) **9**
    5
    4 +
___

9) **6**
    3
    2 +
___

10) **8**
     7
     4 +
___

f. Problem Solving up to 9

Everyday problems often require number sentences to solve them. Problems are usually written in words and need to be converted into figures to solve.

Example: | Paul has **five** chews, Nadine has **two** toffees and James has **one** lollipop. How many sweets do they have altogether?

Paul has **5** chews, Nadine has **2** toffees and James has **1** lollipop. 'Altogether' means a total must be found which requires adding.

Convert the problem into a number sentence.

$$5 + 2 + 1 = 8$$

Answer: **8 sweets**

Exercise 2: 7   Answer the following:

1) Peter and his mum went to the zoo. They saw **three** monkeys, **two** rhinos and **four** snakes.

   How many animals did they see altogether? ____

2) Ronnie is playing snooker. He pots a red ball worth **1** point and a black ball worth **7** points.

   What is his total score? ____

3) There are two ladybirds. One has **four** spots on its back and the other has **three**.

   How many spots are there altogether? ____

4) Sophie is counting the cars that drive past her house. She sees **2** white cars, **4** black cars and **2** green cars.

In all, how many cars does she count? ____

5) Natalie brings **five** pieces of fruit for lunch, Dave brings **one** piece and Mark brings **three** pieces.

How many pieces of fruit are eaten in total? ____

6) The milkman delivers **3** bottles of milk on Wednesday and **4** bottles on Saturday. How many bottles of milk does he deliver over both days? ____

7) In the class there are **four** boys and **two** girls who wear glasses.

How many children wear glasses? ____

8) The family had **2** cups of coffee, **2** cups of tea and **1** glass of juice.

How many drinks did they have altogether? ____

9) Grace is **3** and Jamie is **1**.

What is their combined age? ____

10) On his birthday, Ian is given a present from his parents, a present from his aunt and a present from his brother.

How many presents in all did he receive? ____

Score

2. Two-digit Addition up to 19

a. Basic Addition up to 19

Example: | Add the dots in the three squares and write the number sentence.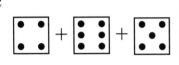

Count the dots in the first square: ⊡. There are **4**.

Count the dots in the second square: ⊡. There are **6**.

Count the dots in the third square: ⊡. There are **5**.

Altogether there are **15** dots.

Answer: **4 + 6 + 5 = 15**

Exercise 2: 8   Add the items and write the number sentence:

Score

1)
_____ + _____ = _____

2)
_____ + _____ = _____

3)
_____ + _____ = _____

4)
_____ + _____ = _____

5)
_____ + _____ = _____

6)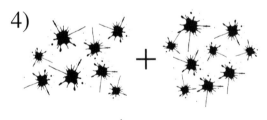
_____ + _____ = _____

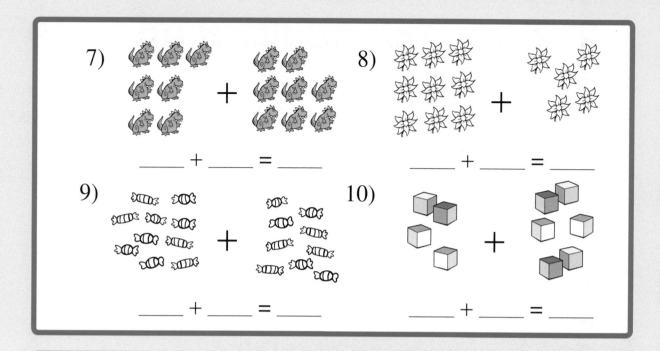

7) _____ + _____ = _____

8) _____ + _____ = _____

9) _____ + _____ = _____

10) _____ + _____ = _____

Example: | Use the number line to calculate **9 + 5**.

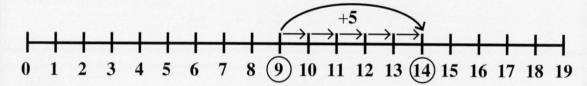

Start at **9** and count **5** places forwards along the number line to reach **14**. The number sentence is: **9 + 5 = 14**

Answer: **14**

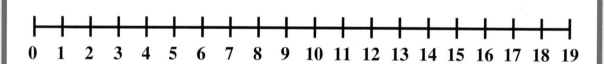

Exercise 2: 9   Use the number line above to answer the following:

1) **7 + 6 =** _____   2) **5 + 9 =** _____   3) **11 + 5 =** _____

4) **16 + 3 =** _____   5) **4 + 13 =** _____   6) **8 + 4 =** _____

7) **12 + 3 =** _____   8) **14 + 5 =** _____   9) **2 + 9 + 5 =** _____

10) **4 + 6 + 8 =** _____   **Score**

b. Number Families up to 19

The total amount of number sentences that form a number family is always one more than the number.

For example, the number family for the number **11** has twelve number sentences because zero has to be included.

Example: Write the number family for the number **10**.

Think of all the numbers that can be added together to make **10**.

Start with **0 + 10 = 10**, then work through the number combinations.

There are eleven number sentences.

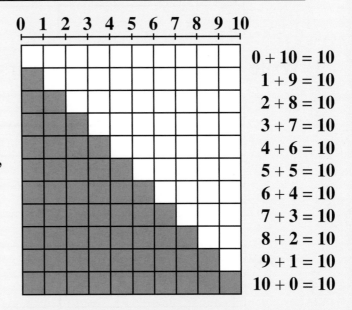

$0 + 10 = 10$
$1 + 9 = 10$
$2 + 8 = 10$
$3 + 7 = 10$
$4 + 6 = 10$
$5 + 5 = 10$
$6 + 4 = 10$
$7 + 3 = 10$
$8 + 2 = 10$
$9 + 1 = 10$
$10 + 0 = 10$

Exercise 2: 10 Complete the number sentences:

1) Write the twelve addition pairs for **11**.

11	
$\underline{0} + \underline{11} = \underline{11}$	___ + ___ = ___
___ + ___ = ___	___ + ___ = ___
___ + ___ = ___	___ + ___ = ___
___ + ___ = ___	___ + ___ = ___
___ + ___ = ___	___ + ___ = ___
___ + ___ = ___	___ + ___ = ___

2) Write the thirteen addition pairs for **12**.

12	
___ + ___ = ___	___ + ___ = ___
___ + ___ = ___	___ + ___ = ___
___ + ___ = ___	___ + ___ = ___
___ + ___ = ___	___ + ___ = ___
___ + ___ = ___	___ + ___ = ___
___ + ___ = ___	___ + ___ = ___
___ + ___ = ___	

3) Write the fourteen addition pairs for **13**.

13	
___ + ___ = ___	___ + ___ = ___
___ + ___ = ___	___ + ___ = ___
___ + ___ = ___	___ + ___ = ___
___ + ___ = ___	___ + ___ = ___
___ + ___ = ___	___ + ___ = ___
___ + ___ = ___	___ + ___ = ___
___ + ___ = ___	___ + ___ = ___

4) Write the fifteen addition pairs for **14**.

14	
___ + ___ = ___	___ + ___ = ___
___ + ___ = ___	___ + ___ = ___
___ + ___ = ___	___ + ___ = ___
___ + ___ = ___	___ + ___ = ___
___ + ___ = ___	___ + ___ = ___
___ + ___ = ___	___ + ___ = ___
___ + ___ = ___	___ + ___ = ___
___ + ___ = ___	

5) Write the sixteen addition pairs for **15**.

15			
___ + ___ = ___		___ + ___ = ___	
___ + ___ = ___		___ + ___ = ___	
___ + ___ = ___		___ + ___ = ___	
___ + ___ = ___		___ + ___ = ___	
___ + ___ = ___		___ + ___ = ___	
___ + ___ = ___		___ + ___ = ___	
___ + ___ = ___		___ + ___ = ___	
___ + ___ = ___		___ + ___ = ___	

6) Write the seventeen addition pairs for **16**.

16			
___ + ___ = ___		___ + ___ = ___	
___ + ___ = ___		___ + ___ = ___	
___ + ___ = ___		___ + ___ = ___	
___ + ___ = ___		___ + ___ = ___	
___ + ___ = ___		___ + ___ = ___	
___ + ___ = ___		___ + ___ = ___	
___ + ___ = ___		___ + ___ = ___	
___ + ___ = ___		___ + ___ = ___	
___ + ___ = ___			

7) Write the eighteen addition pairs for **17**.

17			
___ + ___ = ___		___ + ___ = ___	
___ + ___ = ___		___ + ___ = ___	
___ + ___ = ___		___ + ___ = ___	
___ + ___ = ___		___ + ___ = ___	
___ + ___ = ___		___ + ___ = ___	
___ + ___ = ___		___ + ___ = ___	
___ + ___ = ___		___ + ___ = ___	
___ + ___ = ___		___ + ___ = ___	
___ + ___ = ___		___ + ___ = ___	

8) Write the nineteen addition pairs for **18**.

18			
___ + ___ = ___		___ + ___ = ___	
___ + ___ = ___		___ + ___ = ___	
___ + ___ = ___		___ + ___ = ___	
___ + ___ = ___		___ + ___ = ___	
___ + ___ = ___		___ + ___ = ___	
___ + ___ = ___		___ + ___ = ___	
___ + ___ = ___		___ + ___ = ___	
___ + ___ = ___		___ + ___ = ___	
___ + ___ = ___		___ + ___ = ___	
___ + ___ = ___			

9) Write the twenty addition pairs for **19**.

19			
___ + ___ = ___		___ + ___ = ___	
___ + ___ = ___		___ + ___ = ___	
___ + ___ = ___		___ + ___ = ___	
___ + ___ = ___		___ + ___ = ___	
___ + ___ = ___		___ + ___ = ___	
___ + ___ = ___		___ + ___ = ___	
___ + ___ = ___		___ + ___ = ___	
___ + ___ = ___		___ + ___ = ___	
___ + ___ = ___		___ + ___ = ___	
___ + ___ = ___		___ + ___ = ___	

Complete the number sentence:

10) a) $5 +$ ___ $= 17$ b) ___ $+ 16 = 19$

c) $11 + 7 =$ ___   d) $2 +$ ___ $= 16$

Score

c. Addition in Words up to 19

Example: | Combine **three**, **six** and **seven**. |

Convert the words into a number sentence.

'Combine' is the same thing as using the + sign between the numbers.

The number sentence is: $3 + 6 + 7 = 16$

Answer: **16**

Exercise 2: 11   Answer the following:

1) Add **11** and **6**.   _____

2) Increase **fifteen** by **four**.   _____

3) Find the total of **13** and **2**.   _____

4) What is **3** more than **14**?   _____

5) What is **sixteen** plus **two**?   _____

6) What is **8** and **8** altogether?   _____

7) Find the sum of **9** and **3**.   _____

8) What is the total of **seven** and **five**?   _____

9) Combine **12** and **7**.   _____

Score

10) Increase **9** by **8**.   _____

d. Problem Solving up to 19

Example: | Mr Reynolds is in the supermarket. He selects **two** apples, **five** oranges, **eight** bananas and **three** grapefruit and puts them in his basket. How many items are in the basket in total?

Write the worded numbers as figures to solve.

There are **2** apples, **5** oranges, **8** bananas and **3** grapefruit.

'In total' means a total must be found which requires adding. Convert the problem into a number sentence.

$$2 + 5 + 8 + 3 = 18$$

Answer: **18 items**

Score

Exercise 2: 12 Answer the following:

1) Michael was practising archery. He shot three arrows: one missed the target scoring **zero**; one hit the middle scoring **ten** and one hit an outer ring scoring **six**.

   What was his total score? _____

2) Mollie buys one pack of **12** cakes and Charlie buys one pack of **6** cakes.

   How many cakes do they have altogether? _____

3) A child is given **two** science books, **three** maths books, **three** history books and **three** English books.

   How many books do they have in total? _____

 ae

4) In response to a party invitation, **7** people have said yes, **5** people have said maybe and **3** people have not yet replied.

How many people were invited? _____

5) In an office, **six** people work on computers and **four** people work on telephones.

How many people are there in the office combined? _____

6) On a farm there are **8** chickens, **3** pigs and **6** sheep.

How many animals are there altogether? _____

7) In a building there are **three** rooms on the ground floor, **five** rooms on the top floor and **four** rooms on the first floor.

What is the total amount of rooms? _____

8) There are two friends who are both **7** years old.

What is their combined age? _____

9) In a restaurant there is a table of **five** people placed between a table of **six** people and a table of **eight** people.

How many people are there altogether? _____

10) Annie has a pack of **7** colouring pencils and **6** pens.

How many does she have in total? _____

3. Two-digit Addition up to 99
a. Basic Addition up to 99

Example: Count the dots, write the number sentence and do the calculation.

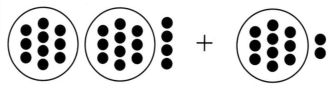

Each circle forms a group of **10** dots.

Count the dots that form the first number: **10 + 10 + 4 = 24**

Count the dots that form the second number: **10 + 2 = 12**

The number sentence is: **24 + 12 = 36**

Answer: **36**

Exercise 2: 13 Write the number sentence:

Score

1)

_____ + _____ = _____

2)

_____ + _____ = _____

3)

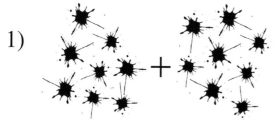

_____ + _____ = _____

4)

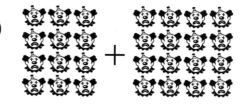

_____ + _____ = _____

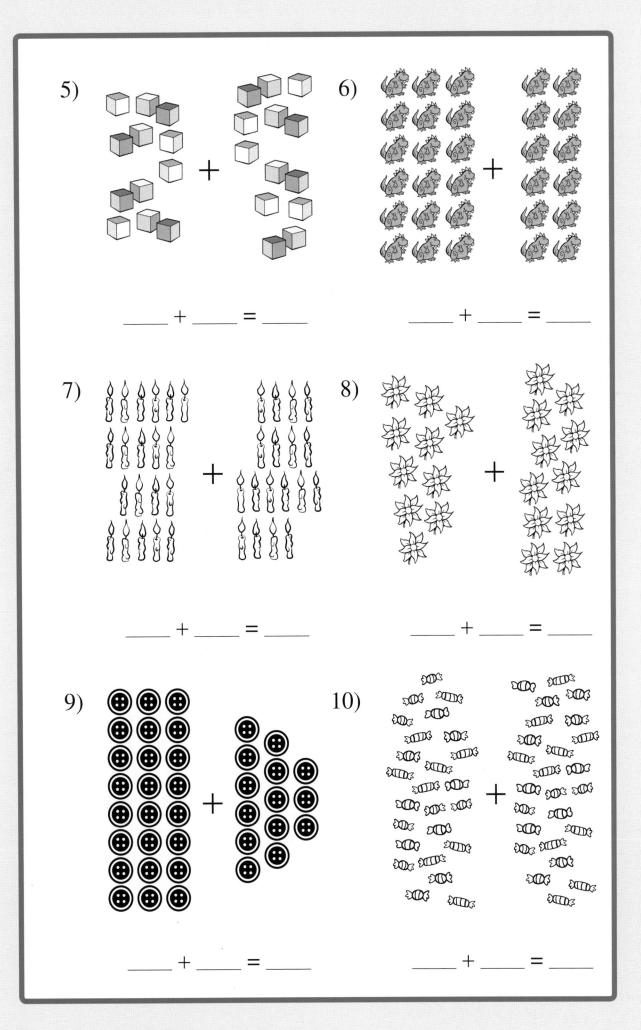

5) ____ + ____ = ____

6) ____ + ____ = ____

7) ____ + ____ = ____

8) ____ + ____ = ____

9) ____ + ____ = ____

10) ____ + ____ = ____

b. Partitioning Numbers

Partitioning means to break up numbers into smaller parts, making calculations easier.

For example, **25** can be partitioned into **20** and **5**.

It can be applied to one or both numbers in a calculation. When adding easier numbers it is possible to partition them into tens and units, which can be added separately.
For example:

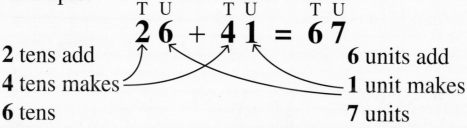

$$\begin{array}{cc} \text{T U} & \text{T U} \quad \text{T U} \\ 2\,6 & +\; 4\,1 \;=\; 6\,7 \end{array}$$

2 tens add
4 tens makes
6 tens

6 units add
1 unit makes
7 units

Example: | Partition and calculate **68 + 25**. |

Step 1 - The numbers can be split into tens and units.

$$\begin{array}{cc}\text{TU} & \text{TU} \\ 68 & + 25 = [60 + 20] + [8 + 5]\end{array}$$

Step 2 - Add the tens and units separately.

$$\begin{array}{cc}\text{TU} & \text{TU} \\ 68 & + 25 = [60 + 20] + [8 + 5] \\ & \qquad\quad 80 \qquad\quad 13\end{array}$$

Step 3 - Add the tens and units together.

$$\begin{array}{cc}\text{TU} & \text{TU} \\ 68 & + 25 = [60 + 20] + [8 + 5] \\ & \qquad 80 \;+\; 13 \;=\; 93\end{array}$$

Answer: **93**

Exercise 2: 14   Partition and calculate the number sentence:

1) **56 + 41** = [_50_ + _40_] + [_6_ + _1_] = _____

2) **82 + 17** = [____ + ____] + [___ + ___] = _99_

3) $49 + 36 = [\underline{\quad} + \underline{\quad}] + [\underline{\quad} + \underline{\quad}] = \underline{\quad}$

4) $27 + 65 = [\underline{\quad} + \underline{\quad}] + [\underline{\quad} + \underline{\quad}] = \underline{\quad}$

5) $13 + 79 = [\underline{\quad} + \underline{\quad}] + [\underline{\quad} + \underline{\quad}] = \underline{\quad}$

6) $34 + 11 + 51 =$

$[\underline{\quad} + \underline{\quad} + \underline{\quad}] + [\underline{\quad} + \underline{\quad} + \underline{\quad}] = \underline{\quad}$

7) $62 + 15 + 21 =$

$[\underline{\quad} + \underline{\quad} + \underline{\quad}] + [\underline{\quad} + \underline{\quad} + \underline{\quad}] = \underline{\quad}$

8) $50 + 27 + 22 =$

$[\underline{\quad} + \underline{\quad} + \underline{\quad}] + [\underline{\quad} + \underline{\quad} + \underline{\quad}] = \underline{\quad}$

9) $31 + 40 + 17 + 6 =$

$[\underline{\quad} + \underline{\quad} + \underline{\quad} + \underline{\quad}] + [\underline{\quad} + \underline{\quad} + \underline{\quad} + \underline{\quad}]$

$= \underline{\quad}$

10) $29 + 12 + 5 + 48 =$

$[\underline{\quad} + \underline{\quad} + \underline{\quad} + \underline{\quad}] + [\underline{\quad} + \underline{\quad} + \underline{\quad} + \underline{\quad}]$

$= \underline{\quad}$

In many easy additions it is only necessary to partition one of the numbers. For example, when adding two-digit numbers, it can be easier to first add the tens and then add the units.

Example: Calculate **27 + 14**.

Instead of adding **14**, it is easier to add **10** then add **4**.

27 + 10 = 37   then   **37 + 4 = 41**   so   **27 + 14 = 41**

Answer: **41**

Exercise 2: 15 Calculate the number sentence:

1) $49 + 11 = $ _____

2) $63 + 24 = $ _____

3) $17 + 35 = $ _____

4) $38 + 21 = $ _____

5) $25 + 13 = $ _____

6) $81 + 14 = $ _____

7) $59 + 32 = $ _____

8) $28 + 22 = $ _____

9) $14 + 15 = $ _____

10) $66 + 25 = $ _____

Example: | Use the number line to calculate $58 + 29$.

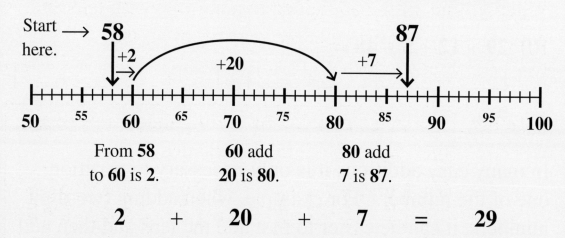

$$2 \quad + \quad 20 \quad + \quad 7 \quad = \quad 29$$

Count **29** units along the number line from **58**, using simple intervals.

The intervals are: add **2**, add **20**, add **7** (totalling **29**). This reaches the answer, **87**.

The number sentence is: $58 + 29 = 87$

Answer: **87**

|++++|++++|++++|++++|++++|++++|++++|++++|++++|++++|++++|++++|++++|++++|++++|++++|++++|++++|++++|++++|

0   5   10 15 20 25 30 35 40 45 50 55 60 65 70 75 80 85 90 95 100

Exercise 2: 16   Use the number line above to answer the following:

1) **34 + 27 = _____**   2) **56 + 11 = _____**

3) **17 + 63 = _____**   4) **72 + 23 = _____**

5) **89 + 5 = _____**   6) **27 + 51 = _____**

Score

7) **48 + 33 = _____**   8) **31 + 67 = _____**

9) **25 + 51 + 14 = _____**   10) **42 + 29 + 13 = _____**

c. Adding 10s up to 99

When groups of ten are added to a number with tens and units there is no change to the number of units.

Example: Do the calculation by adding the groups of ten, then write the number sentence.

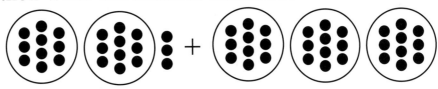

The only numbers that need to be added together are the **2** tens and the **3** tens, which makes **5** tens (or **50**).

The **3** units are then combined with the **5** tens to make **53**.

The number sentence is: **23 + 30 = 53**

Answer: **53**

Exercise 2: 17

Calculate the number sentence:

1) $65 + 30 =$ _____

2) $37 + 40 =$ _____

3) $41 + 20 =$ _____

4) $86 + 10 =$ _____

5) $16 + 70 =$ _____

6) $50 + 43 =$ _____

7) $50 + 29 =$ _____

8) $27 + 60 =$ _____

9) $10 + 48 + 30 =$ _____

10) $34 + 20 + 40 =$ _____

d. Tens Number Bonds

The number sentences for the number family of **20** can be shown on a number line.

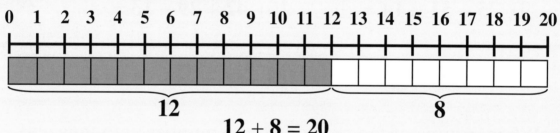

$$12 + 8 = 20$$

For example, to form the number **20** on the number line, **12** is shown in grey and **8** is shown in white.

Example: Fill in the missing number: $18 +$ _____ $= 30$.

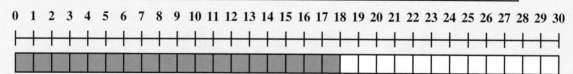

The **18** in the number sentence is represented by the grey squares under the number line. The remaining white squares represent the missing number.

To find the missing number, count along the number line from where the white squares begin.

The number sentence is: $18 + \underline{12} = 30$

Answer: **12**

Exercise 2: 18

Use the number line to fill in the missing number:

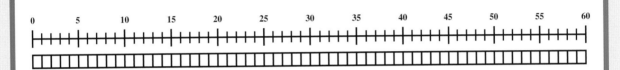

1) $15 + 25 = $ _____

2) $6 + $ _____ $ = 40$

3) $31 + $ _____ $ = 40$

4) _____ $ + 17 = 40$

5) _____ $ + 29 = 40$

6) $55 + $ _____ $ = 60$

7) _____ $ + 24 = 60$

8) $37 + 23 = $ _____

9) $9 + $ _____ $ = 60$

10) _____ $ + 16 = 60$

Score

e. Addition in Words up to 99

Example: What is **eighteen** more than **twenty-six**?

Convert the words into a number sentence. 'More than' is the same thing as using the + sign between the numbers.

The number sentence is: $26 + 18 = 44$

Answer: **44**

Exercise 2: 19 Answer the following:

1) What is **seventy-six** plus **fifteen**? _____

2) Combine **5** and **23**. _____

3) Add **one ten and three units** to **one ten and eight units**. _____

4) Find the total of **25** and **31**. _____

5) What is **12** more than **17**? _____

6) Increase **forty-eight** by **three**. _____

7) Combine **six tens and four units** with **three tens and two units**. _____

8) What is the total of **9** and **28**? _____

9) Find the sum of **nineteen** and **fifteen**. _____

10) What is **8** and **26** altogether? _____

Score

f. Two-column Addition up to 99

Numbers greater than **9** require the use of the tens column.

Addition always starts with the units column followed by the tens column.

Additions can be shown in a horizontal or linear format, such as:

$$\begin{array}{r} \text{Tens} \quad \text{Units} \\ 4\ 2 \\ 3\ 5\ + \\ \hline 7\ 7 \\ \hline \end{array}$$

$$\begin{array}{ccc} \text{T U} & \text{T U} & \text{T U} \\ 42 & + 35 & = 77 \end{array}$$

Example: | Calculate **47 + 23**. |

```
        T  U
        4  7
        2  3 +
        ───────
           0
        1
```

Step 1 - Add the units column.
7 units plus **3** units is **10** units.

Carry the ten leaving **1** ten
and **0** units.

Step 2 - Add the tens column.
4 tens plus **2** tens plus
1 carried ten is **7** tens.

```
        T  U
        4  7
        2  3 +
        ───────
        7  0
        1
```

Answer: **70**

Exercise 2: 20 Calculate the following:

Score

1) 2 6
   1 5 +
────────

2) 3 7
   1 4 +
────────

3) 5 8
   3 5 +
────────

4) 7 4
   1 7 +
────────

5) 8 9
     7 +
────────

6) 6 6
   2 5 +
────────

7) 4 9
   3 2 +
────────

8) 7 7
   1 6 +
────────

9) 5 2
   3 9 +
────────

10) 3 1
    2 9 +
────────

When setting out column additions from number sentences, the larger number goes above and the smaller number goes beneath. It is important to keep the tens and units in line.

ae © 2016 Stephen Curran

Exercise 2: 21   Calculate the following:

1) **24 + 45**

$$
\begin{array}{r}
4\,5 \\
2\,4\ + \\
\hline
\\
\hline
\end{array}
$$

2) **26 + 65**

$$
\begin{array}{r}
6\,5 \\
2\,6\ + \\
\hline
\\
\hline
\end{array}
$$

3) **52 + 45**

$$
\begin{array}{r}
\text{- - - - - - - -} \\
\underline{\qquad}\ + \\
\hline
\end{array}
$$

4) **37 + 46**

$$
\begin{array}{r}
\text{- - - - - - - -} \\
\underline{\qquad}\ + \\
\hline
\end{array}
$$

5) **29 + 70**

$$
\begin{array}{r}
\underline{\qquad}\ + \\
\hline
\end{array}
$$

6) **41 + 57**

$$
\begin{array}{r}
\underline{\qquad}\ + \\
\hline
\end{array}
$$

7) **82 + 12**

$$
\begin{array}{r}
\underline{\qquad}\ + \\
\hline
\end{array}
$$

8) **74 + 21**

$$
\begin{array}{r}
\underline{\qquad}\ + \\
\hline
\end{array}
$$

9) $14 + 62$ 10) $27 + 57$

$$\begin{array}{r} + \\ \hline \\ \hline \end{array}$$

g. Two-column Addition above 99

Example: Calculate $91 + 57$.

Step 1 - Add the units column.
1 unit plus 7 units is 8 units.

$$\begin{array}{r} \text{T U} \\ 9\,1 \\ 5\,7\,+ \\ \hline 8 \end{array}$$

Step 2 - Add the tens column.
9 tens plus 5 tens is 14 tens.
This is 1 hundred and 4 tens.

Carry the hundred, leaving
4 tens in the tens column.

$$\begin{array}{r} \text{H T U} \\ 9\,1 \\ 5\,7\,+ \\ \hline 4\,8 \\ {}_1 \end{array}$$

Step 3 - There are no hundreds to
add, so the carried hundred
is moved into the hundreds
column.

$$\begin{array}{r} \text{H T U} \\ 9\,1 \\ 5\,7\,+ \\ \hline 1\,4\,8 \end{array}$$

Answer: **148**

ae © 2016 Stephen Curran   35

Score

Exercise 2: 22 Calculate the following:

1) 6 3	2) 7 2	3) 9 8	4) 5 7	5) 8 4
5 4 +	4 6 +	7 1 +	5 6 +	5 9 +

6) 5 9	7) 8 1	8) 6 7	9) 7 4	10) 9 9
4 9 +	7 8 +	4 9 +	6 8 +	9 8 +

h. Problem Solving up to 99

Example: | A school group go on a weekend camping trip. They eat **22** cakes on Friday, **17** on Saturday and **34** on Sunday. How many cakes did they eat altogether?

'Altogether' means a total must be found which requires adding. Convert the problem into a number sentence: **22 + 17 + 34**.

It is best to solve this larger problem using column addition.

Answer: **73 cakes**

$$
\begin{array}{r}
3\,4 \\
2\,2 \\
1\,7\,+ \\
\hline
7\,3 \\
\end{array}
$$
1

Exercise 2: 23 Answer the following:

1) Alan plays darts. He throws three darts: the first hits **20**, the second hits **17** and the third hits the bullseye, scoring **50**.

What does he score in total? _____

2) At a barbecue, **ten** burgers, **eight** sausages and **fourteen** chicken drumsticks are cooked.

   What is the total amount? _____

3) Meghan had a series of **12** books, a series of **10** books, a series of **6** books and a series of **13** books.

   How many books did she have altogether? _____

4) There are **18** apples on a tree, **16** pears on a tree and **24** oranges on a tree.

   How many pieces of fruit are there altogether? _____

5) A family bought a loaf of bread with **twenty-four** slices and a smaller loaf of bread with **sixteen** slices.

   How many slices did they have combined? _____

6) A pack contains **40** hairbands. Danica bought **two** packs.

   How many hairbands did she buy? _____

7) A book has **64** pages and a booklet has **16**.

   How many pages are there in total? _____

8) Akinori bought a CD with **42** tracks on it and another CD with **19**.

   How many tracks were there altogether? _____

9) Amelia has one pack of **thirty** pens and one pack of **forty-nine** pencils.

   How many items does she have combined? _____

10) Kai has a pack of **26** marbles. Shane has a pack of **38** marbles.

    How many marbles do they have in total? _____

Score

4. Three-digit Addition
a. Adding 10s and 100s

Example: Calculate **276 + 300.**

The only numbers that need to be added together are the **2** hundreds and the **3** hundreds, which makes **5** hundreds (or **500**).

The **7** tens and **6** units are then combined with the **5** hundreds to make **576**.

The number sentence is: **276 + 300 = 576**

Answer: **576**

Exercise 2: 24 Calculate the following:

Score

1) **481 + 100 =** _____

2) **344 + 300 =** _____

3) **968 + 30 =** _____

4) **704 + 200 =** _____

5) **156 + 600 =** _____

6) **513 + 70 =** _____

7) **260 + 500 =** _____

8) **682 + 10 =** _____

9) **382 + 400 =** _____

10) **222 + 700 =** _____

b. Three-column Addition up to 999

Numbers greater than **99** require the use of the hundreds column.

Additions can be shown in a horizontal or linear format, such as:

Hundreds	Tens	Units
↓	↓	↙

$$\begin{array}{r} 756 \\ 142\,+ \\ \hline 898 \end{array}$$

H T U   H T U   H T U
756 + 142 = 898

Example: Calculate **439 + 382**.

Step 1 - Add the units column.

9 units plus **2** units is **11** units.
This is **1** ten and **1** unit.

Carry the ten leaving **1** ten
and **1** unit.

```
 H T U
 4 3 9
 3 8 2 +
 ─────
     1
 ─────
   1
```

Step 2 - Add the tens column.

3 tens plus **8** tens plus **1** carried
ten is **12** tens.
This is **1** hundred and **2** tens.

Carry the hundred, leaving
2 tens in the tens column.

```
 H T U
 4 3 9
 3 8 2 +
 ─────
   2 1
 ─────
 1 1
```

Step 3 - Add the hundreds column.

4 hundreds plus **3** hundreds plus
1 carried hundred is **8** hundreds.

```
 H T U
 4 3 9
 3 8 2 +
 ─────
 8 2 1
 ─────
 1 1
```

Answer: **821**

Exercise 2: 25   Calculate the following:

1)
```
4 5 2
2 4 7 +
───────

───────
```

2)
```
3 1 8
1 8 5 +
───────

───────
```

3)
```
6 2 4
3 5 9 +
───────

───────
```

4)
```
2 0 6
1 6 2 +
───────

───────
```

5)
```
7 1 1
2 7 6 +
───────

───────
```

6)
```
5 3 0
3 7 1 +
───────

───────
```

7)
```
4 4 4
  9 3 +
───────

───────
```

8)
```
9 7 3
    9 +
───────

───────
```

9) **856 + 107 + 21**   10) **679 + 88 + 9**

   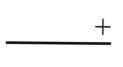

Score

c. Expanded Column Addition

There is an alternative method of doing column addition, known as **Expanded Column Addition**.

It involves adding each column individually and then totalling the answers.

It is useful to know this technique, but standard column addition is a more efficient method.

Example: Calculate **584 + 369**.

```
  H T U
  5 8 4
  3 6 9 +
  ─────
    1 3
```

Step 1 - Add the units column.
  4 units plus **9** units is **13** units.
  This is **1** ten and **3** units.

Step 2 - Put a **zero** in the units column to start in the tens column.

  Add the tens column.
  8 tens plus **6** tens is **14** tens.
  This is **1** hundred and **4** tens.

```
  H T U
  5 8 4
  3 6 9 +
  ─────
    1 3
  1 4 0
```

Step 3 - Put in two **zeros** to start in the hundreds column.

Add the hundreds column. **5** hundreds plus **3** hundreds is **8** hundreds.

```
  H T U
  5 8 4
  3 6 9 +
 _____
    1 3
  1 4 0
  8 0 0
```

Step 4 - Add all three answers together.

$$13 + 140 + 800 = 953$$

Answer: **953**

```
  H T U
  5 8 4
  3 6 9 +
 _____
    1 3
  1 4 0
  8 0 0
 _____
  9 5 3
```

Exercise 2: 26   Calculate the following:

1)
```
  5 6 4
  1 2 5 +
 _____
      9
     80
    600
 _____
```

2)
```
  3 7 6
  2 4 2 +
 _____
      8
    110
    500
 _____
```

3)
```
  6 1 8
  3 2 4 +
 _____
      0
     00
 _____
```

4)
```
  7 6 2
  1 2 7 +
 _____
      0
     00
 _____
```

5) 451
   272 +

   ----

6) 293
   289 +

   ----

7) 761
   149 +

   ----

8) 863
   129 +

   ----

9) 629
   165 +

   ----

10) 555
    357 +

Score

d. Addition in Words up to 999

Example: | Increase **283** by **416**.

Convert the words into a number sentence. 'Increase' is the same thing as using the + sign between the numbers.

The number sentence is **283 + 416**. It is best to solve this addition using column addition and rearranging the order of the numbers.

Answer: **699**

```
  4 1 6
  2 8 3 +
  ─────
  6 9 9
```

Exercise 2: 27 Answer the following:

1) Find the sum of **315** and **81**. _____

2) Increase **sixty-six** by **three hundred and twenty-four**. _____

3) What is the total of **222** and **216**? _____

4) Enlarge **seven tens and eight units** by **eight tens and five units**. _____

5) Find the total of **269** and **54**. _____

6) Combine **ninety-nine** and **six hundred and twenty-one**. _____

7) What is **three tens and six units** plus **one hundred, four tens and two units**? _____

8) Add **256** and **377**. _____

9) What is **twenty-six** more than **one hundred and twenty-seven**? _____

10) Find the total of **six hundred and fifty-two**, **seventy-seven**, **125**, **49**, **sixty-three** and **twenty-three**. _____

Score

e. Three-column Addition above 999

Example: Calculate **763 + 489**.

Step 1 - Add the units column.
      3 units plus **9** units is **12** units.
      This is **1** ten and **2** units.

      Carry the ten, leaving
      2 units in the units column.

$$
\begin{array}{ccc}
H & T & U \\
7 & 6 & 3 \\
4 & 8 & 9 \, + \\
\hline
 & & 2 \\
\hline
 & 1 &
\end{array}
$$

Step 2 - Add the tens column.
      6 tens plus **8** tens plus
      1 carried ten is **15** tens.
      This is **1** hundred and **5** tens.

      Carry the hundred, leaving
      5 tens in the tens column.

$$
\begin{array}{ccc}
H & T & U \\
7 & 6 & 3 \\
4 & 8 & 9 \, + \\
\hline
 & 5 & 2 \\
\hline
1 & 1 &
\end{array}
$$

Step 3 - Add the hundreds column.

7 hundreds plus **4** hundreds plus **1** carried hundred is **12** hundreds.

This is **1** thousand and **2** hundreds.

Carry the thousand, leaving **2** hundreds in the hundreds column.

```
Th  H  T  U
    7  6  3
    4  8  9 +
    2  5  2
    1  1  1
```

Step 4 - There are no thousands to add, so the carried thousand is moved into the thousands column.

```
Th  H  T  U
    7  6  3
    4  8  9 +
 1  2  5  2
    1  1  1
```

Answer: **1,252**

Exercise 2: 28   Calculate the following:

1) 713
    426 +
    _____

    _____

2) 672
    515 +
    _____

    _____

3) 852
    674 +
    _____

    _____

4) 583
    495 +
    _____

    _____

5) 948
    292 +
    _____

    _____

6) 573
    568 +
    _____

    _____

7) 618
    499 +
    _____

    _____

8) 894
    789 +
    _____

    _____

9) 772 + 460 + 39

    _____ +

    _____

10) 999 + 99 + 9

    _____ +

    _____

Score

f. Adding 1,000s and 10,000s

Example: Calculate **11,000 + 4,000**.

The only numbers that need to be added together are the **11** thousands and the **4** thousands, which means that only the **11** and the **4** need to be added.

This makes **15** thousands (or **15,000**).

The number sentence is: **11,000 + 4,000 = 15,000**

Answer: **15,000**

Exercise 2: 29 Calculate the following:

Score

1) **5,000 + 3,000 =** _____   2) **2,000 + 4,000 =** _____

3) **10,000 + 7,000 =** _____   4) **13,000 + 2,000 =** _____

5) **16,000 + 2,000 =** _____   6) **18,000 + 1,000 =** _____

7) **17,000 + 500 =** _____   8) **9,000 + 60 =** _____

9) **4,000 + 800 =** _____   10) **11,000 + 2,000 =** _____

g. Problem Solving

Example: **Four hundred and sixty-three** people live in Darton, **three hundred and eighty-nine** people live in Notton and **ninety-seven** people live in Ryhill. What is the total population?

'Total' means the whole amount must be found which requires adding. Convert the problem into a number sentence: **463 + 389 + 97**.

It is best to solve larger problems using column addition.

Answer: **949 people**

```
  4 6 3
  3 8 9
    9 7 +
  ─────
  9 4 9
  ─────
    2 1
```

Exercise 2: 30   Answer the following:

Score

1) In a sports event, a gold medal is worth **100** points, a silver medal is **75** points and a bronze medal is **25** points. A team won **two** gold medals, **one** silver medal and **one** bronze medal. What was their total score? _____

2) Krisztina bought **two** packs of grapes with **32** in each pack and **two** boxes of raisins with **30** in each pack. How many grapes and raisins are there combined? _____

3) In a game of cricket, the first team scored **235** runs and the second team beat them by **63** runs. How many runs did the second team score? _____

4) A theatre has **550** seats in the stalls, **310** seats in the grand circle and **139** seats in the dress circle. How many seats are there altogether? _____

5) The postman delivered **123** letters in one week, **222** letters in the next and **425** in the third week. How many letters did he deliver in total? _____

6) Inge's aunt gave her a **ninety-piece** cutlery set and a **twenty-one-piece** crockery set. How many pieces were there in total? _____

7) Arosha sends **156** invitations to her family and friends for her wedding to Daniel. As Daniel has such a big family, he decides to send **129** invitations to his family only. How many invitations are sent altogether? _____

8) Kate has **265** DVDs in one rack. She has **302** in another rack and **176** on the shelf. How many DVDs does Kate have in total? _____

9) There are **450** labels in a box. Niamh has one full box, one box with **279** labels in it and a third box with **184** labels in it. How many labels does Niamh have altogether? _____

10) There are **one thousand** children in year 5, **seven hundred and seventy-five** children in year 4 and **three hundred and twenty** children in year 3. How many children are there altogether? _____

5. Mixed Exercises

Exercise 2: 31 Complete the number sentence:

1) ____ + 3 = 7

2) 11 + 5 = ____

3) 17,000 + 2,000 = _____

4) Find the total of **six** and **two**. ____

5) Add the items and write the number sentence:

____ + ____ = ____

Calculate the following:

6) 1 4 8
    2 5
  __1 2 +__

7) 7 5 2
    4 1
  ___6 +__

8) 4 6 7
    3 8 9
  ___2 +__

9) This table shows how many parcels were delivered:

Monday	Tuesday	Wednesday	Thursday	Friday
12	7	6	6	9

How many parcels were delivered in total? _____

10) In a game of bowling, Annie scores **108**, Mair scores **70** and Shai scores **96**. What was the total score? _____

Chapter Three
SUBTRACTION
1. Single-digit Subtraction

Subtraction is the process of counting two or more groups of things and taking one away from the other. This applies to any object, image or number.

It is often represented in a number sentence, such as:

U   U   Units

$$8 - 2 = 6$$

This calculation cannot be written the other way round,

$2 - 8$ does not equal **6**

Number sentences use mathematical symbols.

The symbol for 'subtract' is −.

a. Basic Subtraction up to 9

Example: Write the number sentence and complete the subtraction.

Count the dots in the first square: . There are **5**.

Count the dots in the second square: . There are **2**.

Subtract the lower number from the higher number.

The number sentence is: **5 − 2 = 3**

Answer: **5 − 2 = 3**

Exercise 3: 1

Write the number sentence and complete the subtraction:

1)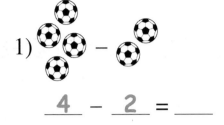

____4____ – ____2____ = _____

2)

_____ – _____ = ___3___

3)

_____ – _____ = _____

4)

_____ – _____ = _____

5) _____ – _____ = _____

6) _____ – _____ = _____

7) _____ – _____ = _____

8) _____ – _____ – _____ = _____

9) _____ – _____ – _____ = _____

10)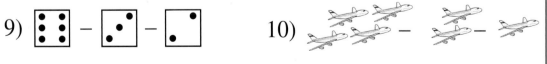

_____ – _____ – _____ = _____

Score

A number line can can also be used for subtracting number sentences.

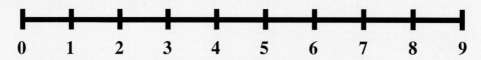

Example: Use the number line to calculate **9 – 4.**

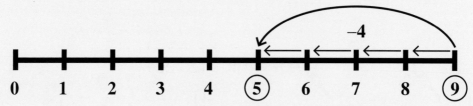

Start at **9** and count **4** places backwards along the number line to reach **5**.

The number sentence is: **9 – 4 = 5**

Answer: **5**

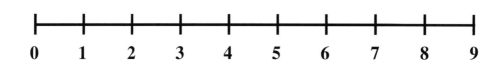

Exercise 3: 2 Use the number line above to answer the following:

1) **8 – 2 =** ___

2) **7 – 5 =** ___

3) **3 – 2 =** ___

4) **6 – 3 =** ___

5) **2 – 1 =** ___

6) **4 – 1 =** ___

7) **9 – 7 =** ___

8) **5 – 2 =** ___

9) **7 – 4 =** ___

10) **9 – 6 =** ___

Score

b. Subtraction in Words up to 9

There are many different terms for subtraction. Here are the most commonly used terms:

- Subtract
- Less
- Minus

- Deduct
- Decrease
- Reduce

- Remove
- Take away/from/off
- Find the difference

Example: | What is **seven** minus **three**? |

Convert the words into a number sentence. 'Minus' means the same thing as using the − sign between two numbers.

The number sentence is **7 − 3 = 4** or **seven** minus **three** equals **four**.

Answer: **4**

Exercise 3: 3   Answer the following:

1) Subtract **three** from **five**. _____

2) Take away **5** from **9**. _____

3) Reduce **eight** by **seven**. _____

4) Minus **one** from **three**. _____

5) Find the difference between **7** and **4**. _____

6) Deduct **one** from **four**. _____

7) What is **6** minus **2**? _____

8) Remove **two** from **two**. _____

9) Decrease **6** by **5**. _____

10) Subtract **zero** from **one**. _____

Score

c. Single-column Subtraction up to 9

Subtraction can be shown horizontally as a number sentence, for example:

U   U   Units
$$8 - 3 = 5$$

Calculations can also be shown vertically. This is called standard column subtraction.

Units
$$\begin{array}{r} 8 \\ 3 \ - \\ \hline 5 \\ \hline \end{array}$$

When laying out column subtraction it is important to keep the numbers in the correct order. The number that is being subtracted always goes underneath.

Always start at the top and work downwards.

Example: Calculate **9 – 6**.

$$\begin{array}{r} 9 \\ 6 \ - \\ \hline ? \\ \hline \end{array}$$

6 is the number being subtracted, so it goes underneath.

9 units subtract **6** units is **3** units.

Answer: **3**

U
$$\begin{array}{r} 9 \\ 6 \ - \\ \hline 3 \\ \hline \end{array}$$

Score

Exercise 3: 4   Calculate the following:

1) $\begin{array}{r} 9 \\ 3 \ - \\ \hline \quad \\ \hline \end{array}$
2) $\begin{array}{r} 5 \\ 2 \ - \\ \hline \quad \\ \hline \end{array}$
3) $\begin{array}{r} 6 \\ 1 \ - \\ \hline \quad \\ \hline \end{array}$
4) $\begin{array}{r} 8 \\ 5 \ - \\ \hline \quad \\ \hline \end{array}$
5) $\begin{array}{r} 7 \\ 4 \ - \\ \hline \quad \\ \hline \end{array}$

6) $\begin{array}{r} 9 \\ 2 \ - \\ \hline \quad \\ \hline \end{array}$
7) $\begin{array}{r} 4 \\ 3 \ - \\ \hline \quad \\ \hline \end{array}$
8) $\begin{array}{r} 8 \\ 6 \ - \\ \hline \quad \\ \hline \end{array}$
9) $\begin{array}{r} 6 \\ 2 \ - \\ \hline \quad \\ \hline \end{array}$
10) $\begin{array}{r} 7 \\ 5 \ - \\ \hline \quad \\ \hline \end{array}$

d. Problem Solving up to 9

Example: Mark has **eight** stickers. He gives **three** to Billy and **two** to Jane. How many stickers does Mark have left?

Mark has **8** stickers.

There are two subtraction sums to be done because Mark is giving away stickers to two other people.

Mark gives **3** to Billy: **8 − 3 = 5**

Mark gives a further **2** stickers to Jane: **5 − 2 = 3**

Answer: **3 stickers**

Exercise 3: 5 Answer the following:

1) Rhys buys **nine** doughnuts but eats **three**.
   How many does he have left? ____

2) Shayne has **8** flowers and Irene has **4**.
   Find the difference. ____

3) There are **six** water bottles in a pack. Osman takes **one**.

   How many water bottles are left? ____

4) There are **five** books on a shelf. Anjali removes **two**.
   How many books are left? ____

5) Nayel has **7** coins but loses **5**.

How many does he have left? ____

6) Asha has **two** dogs, **two** fish and a hamster. Ben has a cat.

Find the difference in the number of pets Asha and Ben have. ____

7) Jaye scores **seven** points. Riddhi scores one less point.

How many points did Riddhi score? ____

8) Katherine watches **6** films in a week. Anna watches **3** films.

What is the difference in the number of films watched? ____

9) Dad has **two** sugars in his tea. Mum has **one**.

How many fewer sugars does Mum have than Dad? ____

10) Jason has **five** brothers and **four** sisters. Hannah has **three** brothers and **one** sister.

Subtract the total number of siblings Hannah has from the number Jason has. ____

Score

2. Two-digit Subtraction up to 19

a. Basic Subtraction up to 19

Example: | Count the number of hearts and take away **6**. Write the number sentence to show the calculation.

There are **14** hearts. Cross out **6** hearts then count how many hearts are left.

Answer: **14 – 6 = 8**

Score

Exercise 3: 6

Write the number sentence and complete the subtraction:

1)

2)

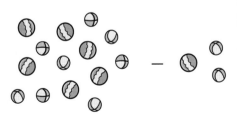

____ – ____ = ____   ____ – ____ = ____

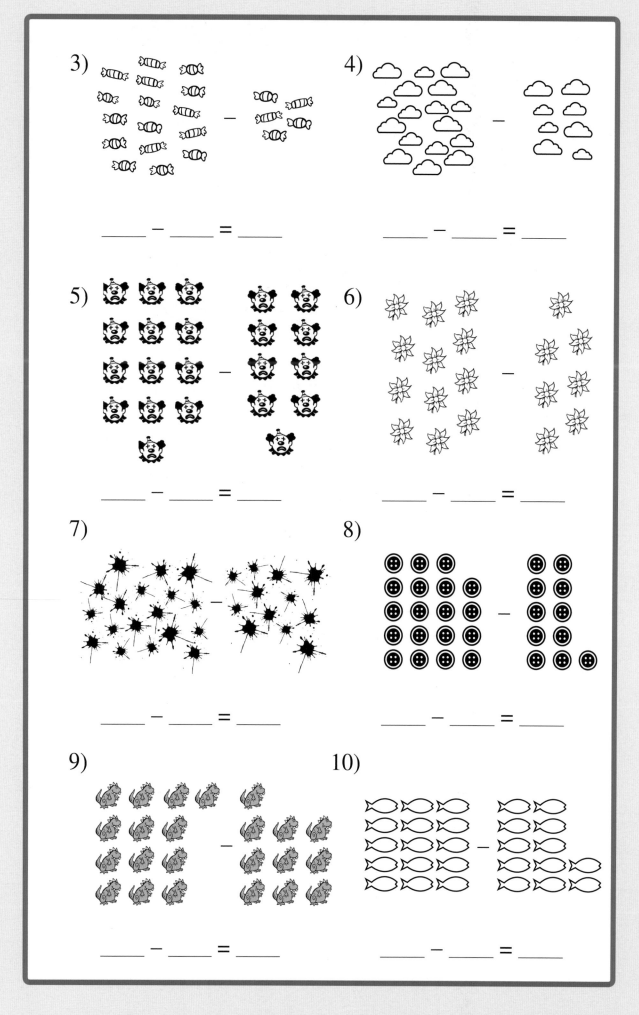

3) _____ − _____ = _____

4) _____ − _____ = _____

5) _____ − _____ = _____

6) _____ − _____ = _____

7) _____ − _____ = _____

8) _____ − _____ = _____

9) _____ − _____ = _____

10) _____ − _____ = _____

Example: Use the number line to calculate **17 – 9**.

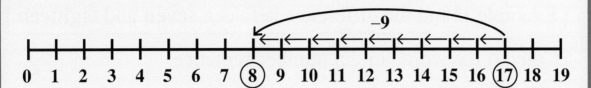

Start at **17** and count **9** places backwards along the number line to reach **8**.

The number sentence is: **17 – 9 = 8**

Answer: **8**

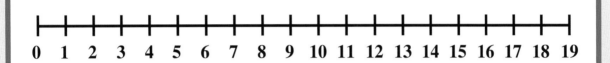

Exercise 3: 7

Use the number line above to answer the following:

1) **19 – 7 = _____** 2) **16 – 8 = _____**

3) **18 – 4 = _____** 4) **15 – 7 = _____**

5) **18 – 6 = _____** 6) **14 – 7 = _____**

7) **12 – 3 = _____** 8) **18 – 9 – 3 = _____**

9) **16 – 8 – 7 = _____** 10) **19 – 6 – 9 = _____**

Score

b. Subtraction in Words up to 19

Example: | Find the difference between **seven** and **eighteen**.

Convert the words into a number sentence.

'Find the difference' is the same thing as using the − sign between the numbers.

When finding the difference between two numbers, the larger number must be placed first.

The number sentence is: **18 − 7 = 11**

Answer: **11**

Exercise 3: 8   Answer the following:

1) Deduct **four** from **seventeen**.   ____

2) What is **2** less than **18**?   ____

3) Reduce **fifteen** by **five**.   ____

4) Subtract **eight** from **nineteen**.   ____

5) Take away **4** from **16**.   ____

6) Decrease **nineteen** by **one**.   ____

7) Remove **3** from **17**.   ____

8) What is **sixteen** minus **one**?   ____

9) Find the difference between **19** and **0**.   ____

10) Take away **one** from **eighteen**.   ____

Score

c. Problem Solving up to 19

Example: There are **nine** tins of beans on the shelf in Mrs Kalia's cupboard. She places **two** tins of tomatoes on the shelf. She then removes **seven** tins of beans. How many tins are now on the shelf?

Write the worded numbers as figures to solve.

There are **9** tins of beans on the shelf and she adds **2** tins of tomatoes.

This number sentence is: **9 + 2 = 11**

She then removes **7** tins of beans.

This number sentence is: **11 − 7 = 4**

Answer: **4 tins**

Exercise 3: 9   Answer the following:

1) There are **nineteen** people in an office.

   If **seven** people have a slice of cake, how many people do not? ____

2) **Eighteen** children in a class like apples. **Six** children like oranges.

   Subtract the number of children who like oranges from the number of those who like apples. ____

3) There are **eighteen** brunettes and **seven** blonde-haired children in a class.

   Find the difference between the number of brunettes and the number of blonde-haired children. ____

4) In a booklet of **16** pages, **3** pages are blank.

   How many pages have writing on them? ____

5) There are **sixteen** pictures on a page and **five** on the next page.

   How many less is this? ____

6) The postman came every day for **14** days. The milkman came **4** times within the same period.

   How many more times did the postman come? ____

7) Amanda picks **13** apples.

   If **3** apples are bruised, how many are not bruised? ____

8) Naimah has **ten** gold stars and **three** sad face stickers. Orlaith has **eight** gold stars and **two** sad face stickers.

   Remove the total number of sad face stickers from the total number of gold stars. ____

9) There are **eight** hamburgers and **eleven** cheeseburgers.

   If Adam eats **five** burgers, how many are left? ____

10) There is a car with **5** seats and a minibus with **14** seats going on a school trip. There are **3** empty seats between the two vehicles.

    How many seats are filled? ____

Score

3. Two-digit Subtraction up to 99

a. Basic Subtraction up to 99

Example: Count the dots, write the number sentence and do the calculation:

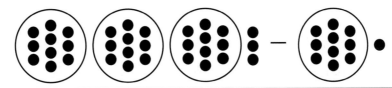

Each circle forms a group of **10** dots.

Count the dots that form the first number:
10 + 10 + 10 + 3 = 33

Count the dots that form the second number: **10 + 1 = 11**

The number sentence is: **33 − 11 = 22**

Answer: **22**

Exercise 3: 10 Write the number sentence:

Score

1)

____ − ____ = ____

2)

____ − ____ = ____

3)

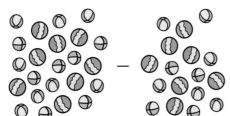

____ − ____ = ____

4)

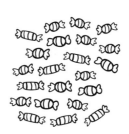

____ − ____ = ____

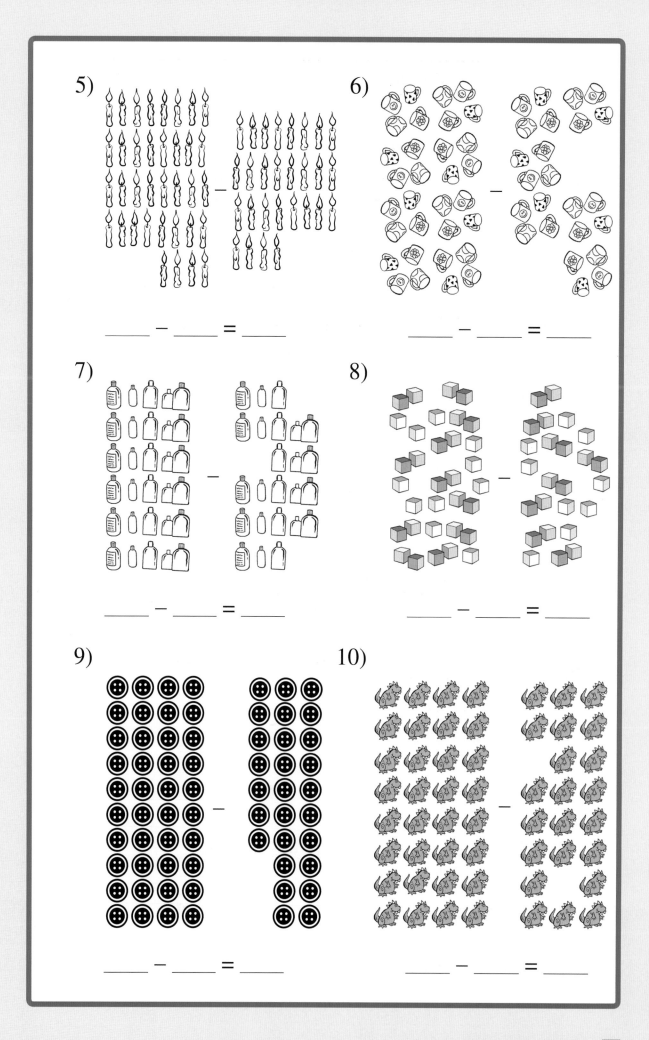

5) _____ − _____ = _____

6) _____ − _____ = _____

7) _____ − _____ = _____

8) _____ − _____ = _____

9) _____ − _____ = _____

10) _____ − _____ = _____

Example: | Use the number line to calculate **43 – 18**.

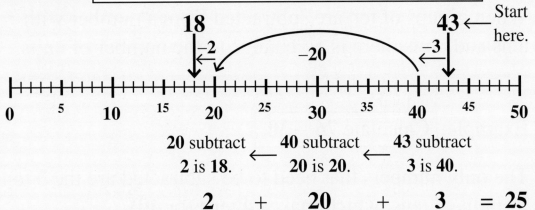

18   **43** ← Start here.

–2   **–20**   **–3**

0   5   **10**   15   **20**   25   **30**   35   **40**   45   **50**

20 subtract   40 subtract   43 subtract
2 is **18**.   **20** is **20**.   **3** is **40**.

2   **+**   **20**   **+**   **3**   **= 25**

To subtract **18** from **43** count backwards along the number line. The intervals are: subtract **3**, subtract **20**, subtract **2**.

To find the difference between **43** and **18**, the intervals must be added together: **2 + 20 + 3 = 25**

The number sentence is: **43 – 18 = 25**

Answer: **25**

---

0   5   **10**   15   **20**   25   **30**   35   **40**   45   **50**   55   **60**   65   **70**   75   **80**   85   **90**   95   **100**

Exercise 3: 11

Use the number line above to answer the following:

1) **96 – 32 =** _____   2) **72 – 24 =** _____

3) **88 – 76 =** _____   4) **54 – 23 =** _____

5) **63 – 18 =** _____   6) **75 – 27 =** _____

7) **94 – 49 =** _____   8) **38 – 21 – 14 =** _____   **Score**

9) **72 – 53 – 16 =** _____   10) **46 – 13 – 25 =** _____

b. Subtracting 10s up to 99

When groups of ten are subtracted from a number with tens and units there is no change to the number of units.

Example: | Calculate **76 – 30**.

The only numbers that need to be subtracted are the **3** tens from the **7** tens, which makes **4** tens (or **40**).

The **6** units are then combined with the **4** tens to make **46**.

The number sentence is: **76 – 30 = 46**

Answer: **46**

Exercise 3: 12   Calculate the following:

Score

1) **70 – 20 = _____**

2) **40 – 30 = _____**

3) **54 – 10 = _____**

4) **81 – 60 = _____**

5) **37 – 20 = _____**

6) **92 – 50 = _____**

7) **68 – 40 = _____**

8) **23 – 10 = _____**

9) **99 – 50 – 10 = _____**

10) **79 – 30 – 20 = _____**

c. Adding and Subtracting 9

An easy way to add **9** is to first add **10** and then subtract **1**. This can be done in reverse when subtracting **9**, by first subtracting **10** and then adding **1**.

Example: | Calculate **48 + 9.** |

Instead of adding **9**, it is easier to add **10** then subtract **1**.

48 + 10 = 58   then   **58 − 1 = 57** ⟶ **48 + 9 = 57**

Answer: **57**

Example: | Calculate **48 − 9.** |

Instead of subtracting **9**, it is easier to subtract **10** then add **1**.

48 − 10 = 38   then   **38 + 1 = 39** ⟶ **48 − 9 = 39**

Answer: **39**

Score

Exercise 3: 13   Calculate the following:

1) **13 + 9 =** _____

2) **56 − 9 =** _____

3) **94 − 9 =** _____

4) **38 + 9 =** _____

5) **25 + 9 =** _____

6) **71 − 9 =** _____

7) **87 − 9 =** _____

8) **42 + 9 =** _____

9) **59 + 9 =** _____

10) **68 − 9 =** _____

d. Adding and Subtracting 11

An easy way to add **11** is to first add **10** and then add **1**. This can be done in reverse when subtracting **11**, by first subtracting **10** and then subtracting **1**.

Example: Calculate **57 + 11**.

Instead of adding **11**, it is easier to add **10** then add **1**.

$$57 + 10 = 67 \quad \text{then} \quad 67 + 1 = 68 \longrightarrow 57 + 11 = 68$$

Answer: **68**

Example: Calculate **57 − 11**.

Instead of subtracting **11**, it is easier to subtract **10** then subtract **1**.

$$57 - 10 = 47 \quad \text{then} \quad 47 - 1 = 46 \longrightarrow 57 - 11 = 46$$

Answer: **46**

Score

Exercise 3: 14   Calculate the following:

1) $27 + 11 = $ _____

2) $43 - 11 = $ _____

3) $82 - 11 = $ _____

4) $15 + 11 = $ _____

5) $39 + 11 = $ _____

6) $94 - 11 = $ _____

7) $70 - 11 = $ _____

8) $51 + 11 = $ _____

9) $66 + 11 = $ _____

10) $78 - 11 = $ _____

ae

e. Partitioning Numbers up to 99

When subtracting numbers it is possible to partition the number that is being subtracted into tens and units.

This means the tens and units can be subtracted separately to give the answer.

For example:

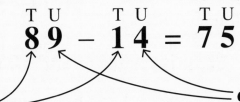

$$\begin{array}{ccc} T\ U & T\ U & T\ U \\ 8\ 9 & -\ 1\ 4\ = & 7\ 5 \end{array}$$

8 tens subtract   9 units subtract

1 ten makes   4 units makes

7 tens   5 units

In most subtractions it is only necessary to partition the second number.

Example: | Partition and calculate **73 – 45**.

Step 1 - Only partition the second   **45** is **40** and **5**
           number into tens and units.   (**4** tens and **5** units)

Step 2 - Subtract the tens. $73 - 40 = 33$

Step 3 - Subtract the units. $33 - 5 = 28$

Answer: **28**

Exercise 3: 15   Calculate the following:

Score

1) **53 – 42**

     42 = [<u>40</u> & <u>2</u>]

     <u>53</u> – <u>40</u> = <u>13</u>

     <u>13</u> – <u>2</u> = ____

2) **87 – 63**

     63 = [<u>60</u> & <u>3</u>]

     <u>87</u> – <u>60</u> = ____

     ____ – <u>3</u> = ____

---

3) **72 – 28**

28 = [_20_ & _8_]

_72_ – _20_ = ____

____ – _8_ = ____

4) **98 – 71**

71 = [_70_ & _1_]

_98_ – ____ = ____

____ – ____ = ____

5) **67 – 39**

39 = [_30_ & _9_]

____ – _30_ = ____

____ – _9_ = ____

6) **74 – 54**

54 = [_50_ & _4_]

_74_ – ____ = ____

____ – _4_ = ____

7) **56 – 29**

29 = [____ & ____]

____ – ____ = ____

____ – ____ = ____

8) **32 – 13**

13 = [____ & ____]

____ – ____ = ____

____ – ____ = ____

9) **96 – 83**

83 = [____ & ____]

____ – ____ = ____

____ – ____ = ____

10) **48 – 17**

17 = [____ & ____]

____ – ____ = ____

____ – ____ = ____

f. Subtraction in Words up to 99

Example: Decrease **72** by **56**.

Convert the words into a number sentence. 'Decrease' means the same thing as using – between the numbers.

When finding the difference between two numbers, the larger number must be placed first.

The number sentence is: **72 – 56 = 16**

Answer: **16**

Exercise 3: 16 Answer the following:

1) Decrease **89** by **17**. ____

2) Take **35** from **64**. ____

3) Find the difference between **ninety-eight** and **forty-five**. ____

4) Reduce **seventy-eight** by **twenty-six**. ____

5) What is **88** minus **49**? ____

6) Subtract **seventy-two** from **ninety-three**. ____

7) Decrease **sixty-seven** by **twenty-four**. ____

8) Remove **37** from **81**. ____

9) What is **twenty-seven** less than **fifty-four**? ____

10) Deduct **forty-four** from **eighty-three**. ____

Score

g. Two-column Subtraction up to 99

When subtracting from a number greater than **9** the tens column must be used.

Subtraction always starts with the units column followed by the tens column.

Subtractions can be shown in a horizontal format, such as:

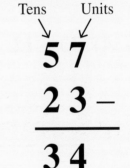

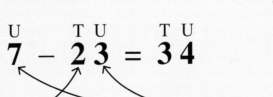

5 tens subtract
2 tens makes
3 tens

7 units subtract
3 units makes
4 units

Example: Calculate **85 – 44**.

T U

8 5

Step 1 - Subtract the units column.

    5 – 4 = **1** unit

4 4 –

1

Step 2 - Subtract the tens column.

    8 – 4 = **4** tens

T U

8 5

4 4 –

Answer: **41**

4 1

Exercise 3: 17   Calculate the following:

1) **94 – 21**

   9 4

   2 1 –

2) **75 – 42**

   7 5

   4 2 –

3) **68 – 37**

   – – – – – –

   – – – – – – –

4) **33 – 12**

5) **87 – 53**

6) **54 – 31**

7) **28 – 17**   8) **49 – 38**   9) **19 – 12**   10) **98 – 35**

If the bottom number in the units column is bigger than the top number, it is necessary to borrow from the tens column.

$$\begin{array}{r} \text{T} \ \text{U} \\ \overset{4}{\cancel{5}}\,\overset{1}{1} \\ 3\,4\,- \\ \hline 1\,7 \\ \hline \end{array}$$

Borrowing is sometimes called decomposition.

For example, **51 − 34 = 17** can be partitioned in the following way:

$$\begin{array}{r} 5\,1 \\ 3\,4\,- \\ \hline \\ \hline \end{array} \rightarrow \begin{array}{r} \text{Tens} \quad \text{Units} \\ 50 + 1 \\ 30 + 4\;- \\ \hline \\ \hline \end{array}$$

Partition the sum into tens and units.

51 is **5** tens and **1** unit

34 is **3** tens and **4** units

1 subtract **4** cannot be done because **1** is smaller than **4**.

$$\begin{array}{r} \overset{4}{\cancel{5}}\,\overset{1}{1} \\ 3\,4\,- \\ \hline 7 \\ \hline \end{array} \rightarrow \begin{array}{r} \text{Tens} \quad \text{Units} \\ 40 + 11 \\ 30 + \;\;4\;- \\ \hline \quad\quad\;\; 7 \\ \hline \end{array}$$

Borrow **1** ten from the **5** tens and change it into units making **10** units. Add this to the units column making **11** units.

11 − 4 = 7 units

$$\begin{array}{r} \overset{4}{\cancel{5}}\,\overset{1}{1} \\ 3\,4\,- \\ \hline 1\,7 \\ \hline \end{array} \rightarrow \begin{array}{r} \text{Tens} \quad \text{Units} \\ 40 + 11 \\ 30 + \;\;4\;- \\ \hline 10 + \;\;7 \\ \hline \end{array}$$

Subtract the tens column.

40 − 30 = 10 units

Add the tens and units columns to give the answer **17** units.

Column subtraction uses the same method but it is simplified, as each stage is not written out.

Example: Calculate **75 – 46**.

Step 1 - Subtract the units column.

5 subtract **6** cannot be done.

Borrow **1** ten from the tens column. Cross out **7** and write **6** because **one** ten has moved to the units column.

Add the borrowed ten to the **5** units making **15** units.

15 – 6 = 9 units

```
  T  U
  6  ¹
  7̸  5
  4  6  –
─────────
     9
─────────
```

Step 2 - Subtract the tens column.

6 – 4 = 2 tens

This gives the answer **29** units.

```
  T  U
  6  ¹
  7̸  5
  4  6  –
─────────
  2  9
─────────
```

Answer: **29**

Exercise 3: 18 Calculate the following:

Score

1) **86 – 67**

```
  ⁷8̸ ¹6
    6 7  –
  ───────

  ───────
```

2) **41 – 29**

```
  4 1
  2 9  –
  ───────

  ───────
```

3) **96 – 78**

```
  - - - - -

      –
  ───────

  ───────
```

4) **33 – 16**

```
  - - - - -

      –
  ───────

  ───────
```

5) **67 – 48**

```

      –
  ───────

  ───────
```

6) **23 – 14**

```

      –
  ───────

  ───────
```

7) **82 – 63**   8) **75 – 48**   9) **57 – 39**   10) **44 – 26**

_____ –   _____ –   _____ –   _____ –

_____   _____   _____   _____

h. Problem Solving up to 99

Example: There were **twenty-eight** people on a bus. At the first stop **nine** people got off and **twenty-three** people got on.

How many people are now on the bus? Give your answer in words.

There were **28** people on the bus and **9** people got off.

The number sentence is: **28 – 9 = 19**

Then **23** people got on the bus.

The number sentence is: **19 + 23 = 42**

Answer: **Forty-two people**

Exercise 3: 19 Answer the following:

1) Tanishk has **70** points. His score decreases by **18** points. What is his new score? _____

2) In three tests Varun scores **twelve** out of **thirty**, **seventeen** out of **twenty-five** and **nine** out of **ten**. How many questions did he get wrong? _____

3) There are **fifty** books on a bookcase. **Ten** are non-fiction, **three** are picture books and the rest are fiction.

How many books are fiction? _____

4) 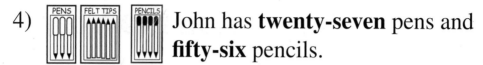 John has **twenty-seven** pens and **fifty-six** pencils.

Find the difference between the number of pens and pencils. _____

5) On a buffet there are **92** slices of cake. **36** people have **two** slices of cake each.

How many slices are left? _____

6) In a year group of **84** children, **48** children are boys.

How many are girls? _____

7) There are **87** people in a swimming pool, **59** of which are adults.

How many children are in the pool? _____

8) In a bowling game Fred scores **ninety-nine** points and George scores **seventy-four** points.

How many fewer points did George score? _____

9) Geoffrey is **83** years old. His grandson is **15** years old.

How many years older is Geoffrey? _____

10) Jimmy needs to learn **eighty-five** spellings for his spelling test. He manages to learn **fifty-eight** spellings.

How many did he fail to learn? _____

4. Three-digit Subtraction
a. Subtracting 10s and 100s

When hundreds are subtracted from a number with hundreds, tens and units, there is no change to the number of tens and units.

Example: Calculate **854 – 600.**

The only numbers that need to be subtracted are the **6** hundreds from the **8** hundreds, which makes **2** hundreds (or **200**).

The **5** tens and **4** units are then combined with the **2** hundreds to make **254**.

The number sentence is: **854 – 600 = 254**

Answer: **254**

Exercise 3: 20 Calculate the following:

1) **727 – 400 =** _____   2) **208 – 100 =** _____

3) **920 – 300 =** _____   4) **863 – 50 =** _____

5) **698 – 500 =** _____

6) **472 – 60 =** _____

7) **319 – 200 =** _____

8) **576 – 40 =** _____

9) **884 – 600 =** _____

10) **985 – 800 =** _____

b. Expanded Column Subtraction

There is an alternative method of doing column subtraction, known as **Expanded Column Subtraction**. This method involves partitioning both numbers and then subtracting each column separately.

Example: | Calculate **524 – 376**. |

Step 1 - Partition the numbers into hundreds, tens and units.

$$
\begin{array}{ccc}
\text{H} & \text{T} & \text{U} \\
5 & 2 & 4 \\
3 & 7 & 6 \;- \\
\hline
\end{array}
\longrightarrow
\begin{array}{ccc}
\text{Hundreds} & \text{Tens} & \text{Units} \\
500 + & 20 + & 4 \\
300 + & 70 + & 6 \;- \\
\hline
\end{array}
$$

Step 2 - Subtract the units column.

4 subtract **6** cannot be done, so borrow **10** from the tens column.

14 – 6 = 8

$$
\begin{array}{ccc}
\text{H} & \text{T} & \text{U} \\
5 & \overset{1}{\cancel{2}} & \overset{1}{4} \\
3 & 7 & 6 \;- \\
\hline
 & & 8 \\
\end{array}
\longrightarrow
\begin{array}{ccc}
\text{Hundreds} & \text{Tens} & \text{Units} \\
500 + & \overset{10}{\cancel{20}} + & \overset{1}{4} \\
300 + & 70 + & 6 \;- \\
\hline
 & & 8 \\
\end{array}
$$

Step 3 - Subtract the tens column.

10 subtract **70** cannot be done, so borrow **100** from the hundreds column.

110 – 70 = 40

Subtract the hundreds column.

400 – 300 = 100

$$\begin{array}{ccc} \text{H} & \text{T} & \text{U} \\ & ^1 & ^1 \\ 41 & 1 & \\ \cancel{5}\;\cancel{2}\;4 & & \\ 3\;7\;6 & - & \\ \hline 1\;4\;8 & & \end{array}$$

Hundreds	Tens	Units
400	110	^{1}
$\cancel{500}$ +	$\cancel{20}$ +	4
300 +	70 +	6 –
100	40	8

Step 4 - Combine the hundreds, tens and units to find the answer.

100 + 40 + 8 = 148

Answer: **148**

Column subtraction uses the same method but it is simplified, as each stage is not written out.

Score

Exercise 3: 21   Calculate the following:

1) **716 – 238 =** _____

$$\begin{array}{ccc} 600 & 100 & ^1 \\ \cancel{700} + & \cancel{10} + & 6 \\ 200 + & 30 + & 8 \; - \\ \hline \end{array}$$

2) **471 – 383 =** _____

$$\begin{array}{ccc} 300 & 160 & ^1 \\ \cancel{400} + & \cancel{70} + & 1 \\ 300 + & 80 + & 3 \; - \\ \hline \end{array}$$

3) 823 – 547 = _____

$$800 + 20 + 3$$
$$500 + 40 + 7 \ -$$
_____

_____

4) 641 – 362 = _____

$$600 + 40 + 1$$
$$300 + 60 + 2 \ -$$
_____

_____

5) 398 – 289 = _____

$+ \quad +$
$+ \quad + \quad -$
_____

_____

6) 635 – 247 = _____

$+ \quad +$
$+ \quad + \quad -$
_____

_____

7) 289 – 199 = _____

$+ \quad +$
$+ \quad + \quad -$
_____

_____

8) 962 – 671 = _____

$+ \quad +$
$+ \quad + \quad -$
_____

_____

9) 527 – 428 = _____

$+ \quad +$
$+ \quad + \quad -$
_____

_____

10) 154 – 129 = _____

$+ \quad +$
$+ \quad + \quad -$
_____

_____

c. Three-column Subtraction up to 999

When subtracting from a number greater than **99**, the hundreds column must be used.

Subtraction starts with the units column, followed by the tens column and then the hundreds column.

Subtractions can be shown in a horizontal or linear format, such as:

Hundreds Tens Units

$$\begin{array}{r} 783 \\ 321\ - \\ \hline 462 \\ \hline \end{array}$$

HTU   HTU   HTU
$$783 - 321 = 462$$

Example: Calculate **844 − 365**.

Step 1 - Subtract the units column.

4 subtract **5** cannot be done.

Borrow **1** ten from the tens column. Cross out **4** and write **3**.

Add the borrowed ten to the 4 units making **14** units.

$$14 - 5 = 9 \text{ units}$$

$$\begin{array}{r} H\ T\ U \\ 8\ \overset{3}{\cancel{4}}\ \overset{1}{4} \\ 3\ 6\ 5\ - \\ \hline 9 \\ \hline \end{array}$$

Step 2 - Subtract the tens column.

3 subtract **6** cannot be done.

Borrow **1** hundred from the hundreds column. Cross out **8** and write **7** because **1** hundred is moving to the tens column as **10** tens.

Add the borrowed hundred to the **3** tens to make **13** tens.

$$13 - 6 = 7 \text{ tens}$$

$$\begin{array}{r} H\ \ T\ \ U \\ \overset{7}{\cancel{8}}\ \overset{13}{\cancel{4}}\ \overset{1}{4} \\ 3\ \ 6\ \ 5\ - \\ \hline 7\ 9 \\ \hline \end{array}$$

Step 3 - Subtract the hundreds column.

$7 - 3 = 4$ hundreds

This gives the answer **479** units.

Answer: **479**

```
        H   T   U
        7  13   1
        8   4   4
        3   6   5  –
        ─────────
        4   7   9
        ─────────
```

Exercise 3: 22   Calculate the following:

1) 748 – 132

```
  7 4 8
  1 3 2  –
  ──────
```

2) 563 – 241

```
  5 6 3
  2 4 1  –
  ──────
```

3) 718 – 426

```
    6  1
  7 1 8
  4 2 6  –
  ──────
```

4) 947 – 896

5) 386 – 159

6) 778 – 569

7) 878 – 699

8) 423 – 348

9) 578 – 389

10) 634 – 276

Score

When subtracting, it is sometimes necessary to borrow twice before starting the calculation.

This is because there are no tens to borrow from in the larger number, so borrowing must occur in the hundreds column.

For example:

$$HTU \quad HTU \quad HTU$$
$$500 - 381 = 119$$

The larger number, **500**, has a **zero** in both the units and the tens columns.

$$
\begin{array}{r}
\overset{4}{\cancel{5}}\overset{\overset{9}{1}}{\cancel{0}}\overset{1}{0} \\
3\,8\,1\,- \\
\hline
1\,1\,9 \\
\hline
\end{array}
$$

H T U

Example: Calculate **700 − 186.**

H T U
$$
\begin{array}{r}
7\,0\,0 \\
1\,8\,6\,- \\
\hline
\end{array}
$$

Step 1 - Subtract the units column.

0 subtract **6** cannot be done.

There are **0** tens, so borrow from the hundreds column instead of the tens column.

Cross out **7** and write **6**.

Add the borrowed hundred to the **0** tens to make **10** tens.

H T U
$$
\begin{array}{r}
\overset{6}{\cancel{7}}\overset{1}{0}\,0 \\
1\,8\,6\,- \\
\hline
\end{array}
$$

Step 2 - **0** subtract **6** still cannot be done, but there are now **10** tens to borrow from.

Borrow **1** ten from the tens column. Cross out **10** and write **9**.

Add the borrowed ten to the **0** units to make **10** units.

10 − 6 = 4 units

H T U
$$
\begin{array}{r}
\overset{6}{\cancel{7}}\overset{\overset{9}{\cancel{1}}}{\cancel{0}}\overset{1}{0} \\
1\,8\,6\,- \\
\hline
4 \\
\hline
\end{array}
$$

Step 3 - Subtract the tens column.

$9 - 8 = 1$ ten

Subtract the hundreds column.

$6 - 1 = 5$ hundreds

This gives the answer **514** units.

Answer: **514**

$$
\begin{array}{r}
\overset{\text{H T U}}{} \\
{}^{6}\cancel{7}\,{}^{9}\cancel{0}\,{}^{1}0 \\
1\ 8\ 6\ - \\
\hline
5\ 1\ 4 \\
\hline
\end{array}
$$

Exercise 3: 23   Calculate the following:

1) **700 – 549**

$$
\begin{array}{r}
{}^{6}\cancel{7}\,{}^{9}\cancel{0}\,{}^{1}0 \\
5\ 4\ 9\ - \\
\hline
 \\
\end{array}
$$

2) **900 – 713**

$$
\begin{array}{r}
9\ 0\ 0 \\
7\ 1\ 3\ - \\
\hline
 \\
\end{array}
$$

3) **800 – 229**

$$
\begin{array}{r}
8\ 0\ 0 \\
2\ 2\ 9\ - \\
\hline
 \\
\end{array}
$$

4) **200 – 179**

5) **300 – 114**

6) **700 – 595**

7) **600 – 338**

8) **500 – 353**

9) **800 – 726**

10) **400 – 226**

$$\begin{array}{r} \\ - \\ \hline \end{array}$$

Score

d. Subtraction in Words up to 999

Example: | What is **975** less **261**? |

Convert the words into a number sentence.

'Less' means the same thing as using the – sign between the numbers.

The number sentence is **975 – 261**. It is best to solve this word subtraction using column subtraction, as shown.

$$\begin{array}{r} 9\,7\,5 \\ 2\,6\,1\,- \\ \hline 7\,1\,4 \end{array}$$

Answer: **714**

Exercise 3: 24 Answer the following:

1) What is **one hundred and sixty-three** less than **eight hundred and seventy-two**? _____

2) Deduct **258** from **632**. _____

3) Remove **132** from **555**. _____

4) Take **one hundred and eight** from **two hundred and eleven**. _____

5) Subtract **378** from **877**. _____

6) What is **two hundred and twenty-two** minus **one hundred and thirteen**? _____

7) Reduce **708** by **278**. _____

8) Decrease **869** by **385**. _____

9) Find the difference between **four hundred and twelve** and **five hundred and thirty-six**? _____

10) Minus **236** from **613**. _____

Score

e. Column Subtraction above 999

When subtracting from a number greater than **999**, the thousands column must be used.

Subtractions can be shown in a horizontal or linear format, such as:

Th H T U   H T U   Th H T U
2,538 − 314 = 2,224

Thousands Hundreds Tens Units

$$
\begin{array}{r}
2\,5\,3\,8 \\
3\,1\,4\, - \\
\hline
2\,2\,2\,4 \\
\hline
\end{array}
$$

Example: │ Calculate **1,340 − 427**. │

Step 1 - Subtract the units column.
     0 subtract **7** cannot be done.
     Borrow **1** ten from the tens column. Cross out **4** and write **3**.
     Add the borrowed ten to the **0** units making **10** units.
     10 − 7 = 3 units

$$
\begin{array}{r}
\text{Th} \; \text{H} \; \text{T} \; \text{U} \\
1\,3\,\overset{3}{\cancel{4}}\,\overset{1}{0} \\
4\,2\,7\, - \\
\hline
3 \\
\hline
\end{array}
$$

Step 2 - Subtract the tens column.

$3 - 2 = 1$ ten

$$\begin{array}{r} \text{Th } \text{H } \text{T } \text{U} \\ 1\ 3\ \overset{3}{\cancel{4}}\ \overset{1}{0} \\ 4\ 2\ 7\ - \\ \hline 1\ 3 \end{array}$$

Step 3 - Subtract the hundreds column.

3 subtract **4** cannot be done.

Borrow from the thousands column.

Cross out **1** and write **0**.

Add the borrowed thousand to the **3** hundreds to make **13** hundreds.

$$\begin{array}{r} \text{Th } \text{H } \text{T } \text{U} \\ \overset{0}{\cancel{1}}\ \overset{1}{3}\ \overset{3}{\cancel{4}}\ \overset{1}{0} \\ 4\ 2\ 7\ - \\ \hline 9\ 1\ 3 \end{array}$$

13 – 4 = 9 hundreds

There is nothing left to subtract in the thousands column. This gives the answer **913** units.

Answer: **913**

Exercise 3: 25   Calculate the following:

1) $\begin{array}{r} 6\ 9\ \overset{4}{\cancel{5}}\ \overset{1}{1} \\ 1\ 1\ 9\ - \\ \hline \end{array}$ 2) $\begin{array}{r} 2\ 8\ 8\ 5 \\ 4\ 6\ 9\ - \\ \hline \end{array}$ 3) $\begin{array}{r} 5\ 3\ 7\ 7 \\ 6\ 8\ 8\ - \\ \hline \end{array}$ 4) $\begin{array}{r} 9\ 4\ 4\ 9 \\ 7\ 5\ 9\ - \\ \hline \end{array}$

5) $\begin{array}{r} 2\ 6\ 8\ 1 \\ 2\ 3\ 5\ - \\ \hline \end{array}$ 6) $\begin{array}{r} 1\ 4\ 6\ 9 \\ 5\ 7\ 8\ - \\ \hline \end{array}$ 7) $\begin{array}{r} 8\ 5\ 2\ 4 \\ 4\ 6\ 9\ - \\ \hline \end{array}$ 8) $\begin{array}{r} 4\ 1\ 8\ 3 \\ 3\ 7\ 4\ - \\ \hline \end{array}$

9) 6 7 2 2
    5 6 6 –
‾‾‾‾‾‾‾‾‾

‾‾‾‾‾‾‾‾‾

10) 3 0 0 3
      4 6 7 –
‾‾‾‾‾‾‾‾‾

‾‾‾‾‾‾‾‾‾

Score

f. Subtracting 1,000s and 10,000s

Example: | Calculate **15,000 – 7,000**. |

The only numbers that need to be subtracted are the **7** thousands from the **15** thousands, which makes **8** thousands (or **8,000**).

The number sentence is:

$$15,000 - 7,000 = 8,000$$

Answer: **8,000**

Score

Exercise 3: 26 Calculate the following:

1) **84,000 – 3,000 =** _____   2) **67,000 – 3,000 =** _____

3) **39,000 – 6,000 =** _____   4) **18,000 – 7,000 =** _____

5) **29,000 – 4,000 =** _____   6) **46,000 – 6,000 =** _____

7) **71,000 – 1,000 =** _____   8) **58,000 – 1,000 =** _____

9) **93,000 – 2,000 =** _____   10) **14,000 – 2,000 =** _____

g. Problem Solving

Example: There are **749** boxes in a warehouse. **468** boxes have blue labels and the rest have red labels. How many boxes have red labels?

To find the missing amount, the number of blue label boxes must be subtracted from the total. Convert the problem into a number sentence:

749 – 468

It is best to solve this larger problem using column subtraction, as shown.

$$\begin{array}{r} ^6\cancel{7}^1 4\ 9 \\ 4\ 6\ 8 - \\ \hline 2\ 8\ 1 \end{array}$$

Answer: **281 boxes**

Exercise 3: 27 Answer the following:

1) The optician's has a total of **two hundred and seventy-six** pairs of glasses. It sells **fifty-three** pairs of children's glasses and **eighteen** pairs of adults' glasses.

   How many pairs are left? _____

2) There are **975** cars on the motorway. **126** are red, **257** are blue and **58** are yellow. The rest are black.

   How many black cars are there? _____

3) Jamie scored **112** runs in a game of cricket. His team scored **565** runs in total.

   How many runs did the rest of his team score? _____

4) There are **five hundred and sixty-eight** seats in a cinema. There are **two thousand** seats in a theatre.

   How many more seats are there in the theatre? _____

5) Sonny goes shopping and buys **165** apples, **27** carrots and **79** bananas.
Find the difference between the total number of fruit and vegetables. _____

6) Tim has **two hundred and thirty-four** phone numbers stored in his phone. He contacts **fifty-eight** regularly. How many does he not regularly contact? _____

7) A bush has **676** leaves and a tree has **488** leaves. Subtract the number of leaves on the tree from the number of leaves on the bush. _____

8) Anthony uses **four hundred and fifty-six** raffle tickets out of **seven hundred and sixty-eight**. How many does he not use? _____

9) A street has **521** houses. **132** houses are occupied. How many are unoccupied? _____

10) 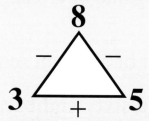 A clothes shop sells **315** tops and **227** pairs of trousers. How many more tops are sold? _____

Score

5. Inverse Operations

It is useful to understand the relationship between addition and subtraction. **Inverse means Opposite.**

+ and − are a pair of inverse operations.

The inverse of addition is subtraction.

$$5 + 3 = 8$$
$$8 - 3 = 5$$
$$8 - 5 = 3$$

For every addition calculation there are two subtractions that relate to it as inverse operations. This can be represented using a triangle.

Example: Show the **3** calculations that link **67**, **42** and **25**.

There are one addition and two subtractions that demonstrate how these numbers relate to each other.

$$\begin{array}{r} 67 \\[-2pt] \overset{-}{}\overset{\triangle}{}\overset{-}{} \\ 42 \quad + \quad 25 \end{array}$$

Addition
42 + 25

$$\begin{array}{r} 4\ 2 \\ 2\ 5\ + \\ \hline 6\ 7 \end{array}$$

1st Subtraction
67 − 42

$$\begin{array}{r} 6\ 7 \\ 4\ 2\ - \\ \hline 2\ 5 \end{array}$$

2nd Subtraction
67 − 25

$$\begin{array}{r} 6\ 7 \\ 2\ 5\ - \\ \hline 4\ 2 \end{array}$$

Answer: 42 + 25 = 67; 67 − 42 = 25; 67 − 25 = 42

Exercise 3: 28 Calculate the following:

1-2)

$$\begin{array}{r} 8\ 8 \\ \boxed{4\ 3}\ - \\ \hline 4\ 5 \end{array} \qquad \begin{array}{r} 8\ 8 \\ \boxed{}\ - \\ \hline 4\ 3 \end{array} \qquad \begin{array}{r} 4\ 5 \\ 4\ 3\ + \\ \hline \boxed{} \end{array}$$

3-4)

$$\begin{array}{r} 3\ 6\ 3 \\ 2\ 1\ 4\ - \\ \hline \boxed{1\ 4\ 9} \end{array} \qquad \begin{array}{r} 3\ 6\ 3 \\ 1\ 4\ 9\ - \\ \hline \boxed{} \end{array} \qquad \begin{array}{r} 2\ 1\ 4 \\ \boxed{}\ + \\ \hline 3\ 6\ 3 \end{array}$$

5-7)

$$\begin{array}{r} \boxed{} \\ 4\ 5\ - \\ \hline 4\ 2 \end{array} \qquad \begin{array}{r} 8\ 7 \\ 4\ 2\ - \\ \hline \boxed{} \end{array} \qquad \begin{array}{r} 4\ 5 \\ \boxed{}\ + \\ \hline 8\ 7 \end{array}$$

8-10)

$$\begin{array}{r} 4\ 8\ 6 \\ 1\ 6\ 2\ - \\ \hline \boxed{} \end{array} \qquad \begin{array}{r} \boxed{} \\ 3\ 2\ 4\ - \\ \hline 1\ 6\ 2 \end{array} \qquad \begin{array}{r} 3\ 2\ 4 \\ \boxed{}\ + \\ \hline 4\ 8\ 6 \end{array}$$

Score

6. Mixed Exercises

Exercise 3: 29 Calculate the following:

Score

1) Subtract the items and write the number sentence:

____ – ____ – ____ = ____

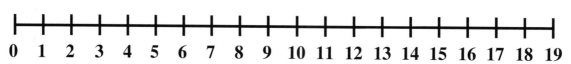

0 1 2 3 4 5 6 7 8 9 10 11 12 13 14 15 16 17 18 19

Use the number line to answer the question:

2) **18 – 7 – 4 =** ____

3) Partition and calculate **67 – 48**:

   48 = [____ & ____]

   ___ – ___ = ____

   ___ – ___ = ____

4) $\begin{array}{r} 9\,5\,6\,8 \\ 1\,3\,4\ - \\ \hline \\ \hline \end{array}$

5) Find the difference between **six hundred and four** and **three hundred and seventy-one**. _____

6) Calculate the following:

   709 – 262 = _____

   $\begin{array}{r} 700 + \ \ 0 + 9 \\ 200 + 60 + 2\ - \\ \hline \\ \hline \end{array}$

7) At Christmas, a family buys a box of **100** gift labels. If Mum uses **42** labels and Dad uses **21**, how many labels are left? _____

8-10)

$\begin{array}{r} 5\,7\,8 \\ 2\,6\,4\ - \\ \hline \boxed{} \end{array}$
$\qquad$
$\begin{array}{r} \boxed{} \\ 3\,1\,4\ - \\ \hline 2\,6\,4 \end{array}$
$\qquad$
$\begin{array}{r} 3\,1\,4 \\ \boxed{}\ + \\ \hline 5\,7\,8 \end{array}$

Answers

Chapter Two
Addition

Exercise 2: 1
1) $5 + 1 = 6$
2) $1 + 1 = 2$
3) $2 + 2 = 4$
4) $2 + 1 = 3$
5) $2 + 6 = 8$
6) $4 + 3 = 7$
7) $1 + 2 + 2 = 5$
8) $4 + 1 + 2 = 7$
9) $3 + 1 + 5 = 9$
10) $2 + 3 + 3 = 8$

Exercise 2: 2
1) 5   2) 5
3) 7   4) 9
5) 8   6) 7
7) 9   8) 8
9) 8   10) 9

Exercise 2: 3a
1) $0 + 4 = 4$
$1 + 3 = 4$
$2 + 2 = 4$
$3 + 1 = 4$
$4 + 0 = 4$
2) $0 + 5 = 5$
$1 + 4 = 5$
$2 + 3 = 5$
$3 + 2 = 5$
$4 + 1 = 5$
$5 + 0 = 5$
3) $0 + 6 = 6$
$1 + 5 = 6$
$2 + 4 = 6$
$3 + 3 = 6$
$4 + 2 = 6$
$5 + 1 = 6$
$6 + 0 = 6$

4) $0 + 7 = 7$
$1 + 6 = 7$
$2 + 5 = 7$
$3 + 4 = 7$
$4 + 3 = 7$
$5 + 2 = 7$
$6 + 1 = 7$
$7 + 0 = 7$
5) $0 + 8 = 8$
$1 + 7 = 8$
$2 + 6 = 8$
$3 + 5 = 8$
$4 + 4 = 8$
$5 + 3 = 8$
$6 + 2 = 8$
$7 + 1 = 8$
$8 + 0 = 8$
6) $0 + 9 = 9$
$1 + 8 = 9$
$2 + 7 = 9$
$3 + 6 = 9$
$4 + 5 = 9$
$5 + 4 = 9$
$6 + 3 = 9$
$7 + 2 = 9$
$8 + 1 = 9$
$9 + 0 = 9$

Exercise 2: 3b
7) a) 2   b) 0
c) 9   d) 2
8) a) 1   b) 5
c) 5   d) 6

Exercise 2: 3c
9) a) 2 and 0
b) 3 and 3
c) 5 and 2
d) 2 and 1
10) a) 0 and 4
b) 1 and 4
c) 5 and 4
d) 5 and 3

Exercise 2: 4
1) 9   2) 8
3) 3   4) 7
5) 9   6) 6
7) 8   8) 5
9) 4   10) 7

Exercise 2: 5
1) 7   2) 4
3) 4   4) 9
5) 7   6) 2
7) 6   8) 9
9) 8   10) 9

Exercise 2: 6
1) 11   2) 13
3) 15   4) 12
5) 10   6) 13
7) 14   8) 18
9) 11   10) 19

Exercise 2: 7
1) 9   2) 8
3) 7   4) 8
5) 9   6) 7
7) 6   8) 5
9) 4   10) 3

Exercise 2: 8
1) $5 + 6 = 11$
2) $8 + 5 = 13$
3) $9 + 7 = 16$
4) $8 + 9 = 17$
5) $6 + 6 = 12$
6) $9 + 9 = 18$
7) $7 + 8 = 15$
8) $9 + 5 = 14$
9) $10 + 9 = 19$
10) $4 + 6 = 10$

Exercise 2: 9
1) 13   2) 14
3) 16   4) 19

5) 17   6) 12
7) 15   8) 19
9) 16   10) 18

Exercise 2: 10
1) $0 + 11 = 11$
$1 + 10 = 11$
$2 + 9 = 11$
$3 + 8 = 11$
$4 + 7 = 11$
$5 + 6 = 11$
$6 + 5 = 11$
$7 + 4 = 11$
$8 + 3 = 11$
$9 + 2 = 11$
$10 + 1 = 11$
$11 + 0 = 11$

2) $0 + 12 = 12$
$1 + 11 = 12$
$2 + 10 = 12$
$3 + 9 = 12$
$4 + 8 = 12$
$5 + 7 = 12$
$6 + 6 = 12$
$7 + 5 = 12$
$8 + 4 = 12$
$9 + 3 = 12$
$10 + 2 = 12$
$11 + 1 = 12$
$12 + 0 = 12$

3) $0 + 13 = 13$
$1 + 12 = 13$
$2 + 11 = 13$
$3 + 10 = 13$
$4 + 9 = 13$
$5 + 8 = 13$
$6 + 7 = 13$
$7 + 6 = 13$
$8 + 5 = 13$
$9 + 4 = 13$
$10 + 3 = 13$
$11 + 2 = 13$
$12 + 1 = 13$
$13 + 0 = 13$

4) $0 + 14 = 14$
$1 + 13 = 14$
$2 + 12 = 14$
$3 + 11 = 14$
$4 + 10 = 14$
$5 + 9 = 14$
$6 + 8 = 14$
$7 + 7 = 14$
$8 + 6 = 14$
$9 + 5 = 14$
$10 + 4 = 14$
$11 + 3 = 14$
$12 + 2 = 14$
$13 + 1 = 14$
$14 + 0 = 14$

5) $0 + 15 = 15$
$1 + 14 = 15$
$2 + 13 = 15$
$3 + 12 = 15$
$4 + 11 = 15$
$5 + 10 = 15$
$6 + 9 = 15$
$7 + 8 = 15$
$8 + 7 = 15$
$9 + 6 = 15$
$10 + 5 = 15$
$11 + 4 = 15$
$12 + 3 = 15$
$13 + 2 = 15$
$14 + 1 = 15$
$15 + 0 = 15$

6) $0 + 16 = 16$
$1 + 15 = 16$
$2 + 14 = 16$
$3 + 13 = 16$

Answers

4 + 12 = 16
5 + 11 = 16
6 + 10 = 16
7 + 9 = 16
8 + 8 = 16
9 + 7 = 16
10 + 6 = 16
11 + 5 = 16
12 + 4 = 16
13 + 3 = 16
14 + 2 = 16
15 + 1 = 16
16 + 0 = 16

7) 0 + 17 = 17
1 + 16 = 17
2 + 15 = 17
3 + 14 = 17
4 + 13 = 17
5 + 12 = 17
6 + 11 = 17
7 + 10 = 17
8 + 9 = 17
9 + 8 = 17
10 + 7 = 17
11 + 6 = 17
12 + 5 = 17
13 + 4 = 17
14 + 3 = 17
15 + 2 = 17
16 + 1 = 17
17 + 0 = 17

8) 0 + 18 = 18
1 + 17 = 18
2 + 16 = 18
3 + 15 = 18
4 + 14 = 18
5 + 13 = 18
6 + 12 = 18
7 + 11 = 18
8 + 10 = 18

9 + 9 = 18
10 + 8 = 18
11 + 7 = 18
12 + 6 = 18
13 + 5 = 18
14 + 4 = 18
15 + 3 = 18
16 + 2 = 18
17 + 1 = 18
18 + 0 = 18

9) 0 + 19 = 19
1 + 18 = 19
2 + 17 = 19
3 + 16 = 19
4 + 15 = 19
5 + 14 = 19
6 + 13 = 19
7 + 12 = 19
8 + 11 = 19
9 + 10 = 19
10 + 9 = 19
11 + 8 = 19
12 + 7 = 19
13 + 6 = 19
14 + 5 = 19
15 + 4 = 19
16 + 3 = 19
17 + 2 = 19
18 + 1 = 19
19 + 0 = 19

10) a) 12 b) 3
c) 18 d) 14

Exercise 2: 11

1) 17   2) 19
3) 15   4) 17
5) 18   6) 16
7) 12   8) 12
9) 19   10) 17

Exercise 2: 12

1) 16   2) 18
3) 11   4) 15
5) 10   6) 17
7) 12   8) 14
9) 19   10) 13

Exercise 2: 13

1) 8 + 8 = 16
2) 12 + 16 = 28
3) 11 + 14 = 25
4) 16 + 13 = 29
5) 12 + 13 = 25
6) 18 + 12 = 30
7) 20 + 18 = 38
8) 10 + 11 = 21
9) 24 + 14 = 38
10) 25 + 25 = 50

Exercise 2: 14

1) [50 + 40] + [6 + 1] = 97
2) [80 + 10] + [2 + 7] = 99
3) [40 + 30] + [9 + 6] = 85
4) [20 + 60] + [7 + 5] = 92
5) [10 + 70] + [3 + 9] = 92
6) [30 + 10 + 50] + [4 + 1 + 1] = 96
7) [60 + 10 + 20] + [2 + 5 + 1] = 98
8) [50 + 20 + 20] + [0 + 7 + 2] = 99
9) [30 + 40 + 10 + 0] + [1 + 0 + 7 + 6] = 94
10) [20 + 10 + 0 + 40] + [9 + 2 + 5 + 8] = 94

Exercise 2: 15

1) 60   2) 87
3) 52   4) 59
5) 38   6) 95
7) 91   8) 50
9) 29   10) 91

Exercise 2: 16

1) 61   2) 67
3) 80   4) 95
5) 94   6) 78
7) 81   8) 98
9) 90   10) 84

Exercise 2: 17

1) 95   2) 77
3) 61   4) 96
5) 86   6) 93
7) 79   8) 87
9) 88   10) 94

Exercise 2: 18

1) 40   2) 34
3) 9   4) 23
5) 11   6) 5
7) 36   8) 60
9) 51   10) 44

Exercise 2: 19

1) 91   2) 28
3) 31   4) 56
5) 29   6) 51
7) 96   8) 37
9) 34   10) 34

Exercise 2: 20

1) 41   2) 51
3) 93   4) 91
5) 96   6) 91
7) 81   8) 93
9) 91   10) 60

Exercise 2: 21

1) 69   2) 91

Answers

3) 97   4) 83
5) 99   6) 98
7) 94   8) 95
9) 76   10) 84

Exercise 2: 22
1) 117   2) 118
3) 169   4) 113
5) 143   6) 108
7) 159   8) 116
9) 142   10) 197

Exercise 2: 23
1) 87   2) 32
3) 41   4) 58
5) 40   6) 80
7) 80   8) 61
9) 79   10) 64

Exercise 2: 24
1) 581   2) 644
3) 998   4) 904
5) 756   6) 583
7) 760   8) 692
9) 782   10) 922

Exercise 2: 25
1) 699   2) 503
3) 983   4) 368
5) 987   6) 901
7) 537   8) 982
9) 984   10) 776

Exercise 2: 26
1) 689   2) 618
3) 942   4) 889
5) 723   6) 582
7) 910   8) 992
9) 794   10) 912

Exercise 2: 27
1) 396   2) 390
3) 438   4) 163
5) 323   6) 720

7) 178   8) 633
9) 153   10) 989

Exercise 2: 28
1) 1,139   2) 1,187
3) 1,526   4) 1,078
5) 1,240   6) 1,141
7) 1,117   8) 1,683
9) 1,271   10) 1,107

Exercise 2: 29
1) 8,000
2) 6,000
3) 17,000
4) 15,000
5) 18,000
6) 19,000
7) 17,500
8) 9,060
9) 4,800
10) 13,000

Exercise 2: 30
1) 300   2) 124
3) 298   4) 999
5) 770   6) 111
7) 285   8) 743
9) 913
10) 2,095

Exercise 2: 31
1) 4   2) 16
3) 19,000   4) 8
5) $5 + 9 = 14$
6) 185   7) 799
8) 858   9) 40
10) 274

Chapter Three
Subtraction
Exercise 3: 1
1) $4 - 2 = 2$
2) $6 - 3 = 3$

3) $7 - 4 = 3$
4) $6 - 5 = 1$
5) $3 - 2 = 1$
6) $8 - 1 = 7$
7) $6 - 4 = 2$
8) $2 - 1 - 1 = 0$
9) $6 - 3 - 2 = 1$
10) $4 - 2 - 1 = 1$

Exercise 3: 2
1) 6   2) 2
3) 1   4) 3
5) 1   6) 3
7) 2   8) 3
9) 3   10) 3

Exercise 3: 3
1) 2   2) 4
3) 1   4) 2
5) 3   6) 3
7) 4   8) 0
9) 1   10) 1

Exercise 3: 4
1) 6   2) 3
3) 5   4) 3
5) 3   6) 7
7) 1   8) 2
9) 4   10) 2

Exercise 3: 5
1) 6   2) 4
3) 5   4) 3
5) 2   6) 4
7) 6   8) 3
9) 1   10) 5

Exercise 3: 6
1) $18 - 4 = 14$
2) $14 - 3 = 11$
3) $16 - 5 = 11$
4) $17 - 8 = 9$
5) $13 - 9 = 4$
6) $12 - 7 = 5$

7) $18 - 12 = 6$
8) $19 - 11 = 8$
9) $13 - 10 = 3$
10) $15 - 12 = 3$

Exercise 3: 7
1) 12   2) 8
3) 14   4) 8
5) 12   6) 7
7) 9   8) 6
9) 1   10) 4

Exercise 3: 8
1) 13   2) 16
3) 10   4) 11
5) 12   6) 18
7) 14   8) 15
9) 19   10) 17

Exercise 3: 9
1) 12   2) 12
3) 11   4) 13
5) 11   6) 10
7) 10   8) 13
9) 14   10) 16

Exercise 3: 10
1) $19 - 6 = 13$
2) $20 - 18 = 2$
3) $23 - 17 = 6$
4) $22 - 11 = 11$
5) $36 - 28 = 8$
6) $32 - 24 = 8$
7) $30 - 24 = 6$
8) $33 - 25 = 8$
9) $40 - 27 = 13$
10) $32 - 22 = 10$

Exercise 3: 11
1) 64   2) 48
3) 12   4) 31
5) 45   6) 48
7) 45   8) 3
9) 3   10) 8

Answers

Exercise 3: 12
1) 50   2) 10
3) 44   4) 21
5) 17   6) 42
7) 28   8) 13
9) 39 10) 29

Exercise 3: 13
1) 22   2) 47
3) 85   4) 47
5) 34   6) 62
7) 78   8) 51
9) 68 10) 59

Exercise 3: 14
1) 38   2) 32
3) 71   4) 26
5) 50   6) 83
7) 59   8) 62
9) 77 10) 67

Exercise 3: 15
1) 42 = [40 & 2]
   53 − 40 = 13
   13 − 2 = 11
2) 63 = [60 & 3]
   87 − 60 = 27
   27 − 3 = 24
3) 28 = [20 & 8]
   72 − 20 = 52
   52 − 8 = 44
4) 71 = [70 & 1]
   98 − 70 = 28
   28 − 1 = 27
5) 39 = [30 & 9]
   67 − 30 = 37
   37 − 9 = 28
6) 54 = [50 & 4]
   74 − 50 = 24
   24 − 4 = 20
7) 29 = [20 & 9]
   56 − 20 = 36
   36 − 9 = 27

8) 13 = [10 & 3]
   32 − 10 = 22
   22 − 3 = 19
9) 83 = [80 & 3]
   96 − 80 = 16
   16 − 3 = 13
10) 17 = [10 & 7]
   48 − 10 = 38
   38 − 7 = 31

Exercise 3: 16
1) 72   2) 29
3) 53   4) 52
5) 39   6) 21
7) 43   8) 44
9) 27 10) 39

Exercise 3: 17
1) 73   2) 33
3) 31   4) 21
5) 34   6) 23
7) 11   8) 11
9) 7   10) 63

Exercise 3: 18
1) 19   2) 12
3) 18   4) 17
5) 19   6) 9
7) 19   8) 27
9) 18 10) 18

Exercise 3: 19
1) 52   2) 27
3) 37   4) 29
5) 20   6) 36
7) 28   8) 25
9) 68 10) 27

Exercise 3: 20
1) 327 2) 108
3) 620 4) 813
5) 198 6) 412
7) 119 8) 536
9) 284 10) 185

Exercise 3: 21
1) 478 2) 88
3) 276 4) 279
5) 109 6) 388
7) 90   8) 291
9) 99 10) 25

Exercise 3: 22
1) 616 2) 322
3) 292 4) 51
5) 227 6) 209
7) 179 8) 75
9) 189 10) 358

Exercise 3: 23
1) 151 2) 187
3) 571 4) 21
5) 186 6) 105
7) 262 8) 147
9) 74 10) 174

Exercise 3: 24
1) 709 2) 374
3) 423 4) 103
5) 499 6) 109
7) 430 8) 484
9) 124 10) 377

Exercise 3: 25
1) 6,832 2) 2,416
3) 4,689 4) 8,690
5) 2,446 6) 891
7) 8,055 8) 3,809
9) 6,156 10) 2,536

Exercise 3: 26
1) 81,000
2) 64,000
3) 33,000
4) 11,000
5) 25,000
6) 40,000
7) 70,000

8) 57,000
9) 91,000
10) 12,000

Exercise 3: 27
1) 205
2) 534
3) 453
4) 1,432
5) 217
6) 176
7) 188
8) 312
9) 389
10) 88

Exercise 3: 28
1) 45
2) 88
3) 214
4) 149
5) 87
6) 45
7) 42
8) 324
9) 486
10) 162

Exercise 3: 29
1) 5 − 2 − 1 = 2
2) 7
3) 19
4) 9,434
5) 233
6) 447
7) 37
8) 314
9) 578
10) 264

PROGRESS CHARTS

Shade in your score for each exercise on the graph. Add up for your total score.

2. ADDITION

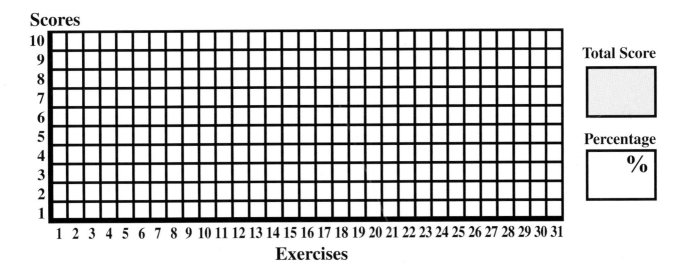

3. SUBTRACTION

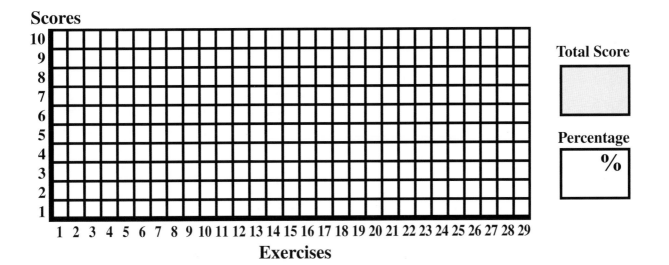

Overall Percentage [%]

CERTIFICATE OF

ACHIEVEMENT

This certifies

_____

has successfully completed

Key Stage 2 Maths
Year 3/4
WORKBOOK **2**

Overall percentage
score achieved
[   ] **%**

Comment _____

_____

Signed _____

(teacher/parent/guardian)

Date _____